Case Manag
Mental Health

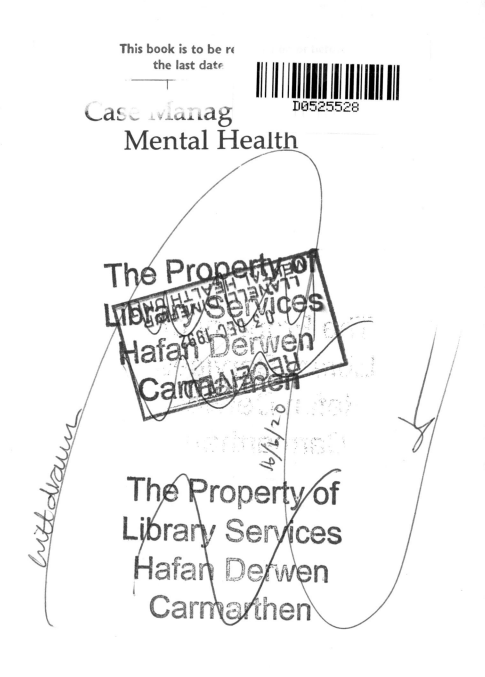

Case Management in Mental Health

Steve Onyett

Team Work Project Manager
Research and Development for Psychiatry,
London;
Head of Rehabilitation Speciality
The Community Care Psychology Specialty
All Saints Hospital
Chatham
UK

CHAPMAN & HALL

London · Glasgow · New York · Tokyo · Melbourne · Madras

Published by Chapman & Hall, 2–6 Boundary Row, London SE1 8HN

Chapman & Hall, 2–6 Boundary Row, London SE1 8HN, UK

Chapman & Hall, 29 West 35th Street, New York NY10001, USA

Chapman & Hall Japan, Thomson Publishing Japan, Hirakawacho Nemoto Building, 7F, 1-7-11 Hirakawa-cho, Chiyoda-ku, Tokyo 102, Japan

Chapman & Hall Australia, Thomas Nelson Australia, 102 Dodds Street, South Melbourne, Victoria 3205, Australia

Chapman & Hall India, R. Seshadri, 32 Second Main Road, CIT East, Madras 600 035, India

Distributed in the USA and Canada by Singular Publishing Group Inc., 4284 41st Street, San Diego, California 92105

First edition 1992

© 1992 Chapman & Hall

Typeset in 10/12pt Palatino by Best-set Typesetter Ltd., Hong Kong
Printed in Great Britain by Page Bros (Norwich) Ltd

0 412 39330 1   1 56593 018 5 (USA)

A catalogue record for this book is available from the British Library

For Jane

Contents

Acknowledgements

I am deeply grateful to those members of the Early Intervention Service who showed me the pleasure and pain of sharing an open-plan office. Steve Malone, Peter Tyrer, Duncan Sellers, Jane Rennison, Shanti Parslow, Jayne Connolly, Nessie Shia and Tom Davey all took an active part in the research and the writing of the case examples.

I am particularly grateful for comments on earlier drafts of the chapters to Paul Cambridge from the Personal Social Services Research Unit, Steve Malone and my partner Jane (who more than anyone can be relied upon not to pull any punches). This book was written during my time at the Centre for the Applied Psychology of Social Care at the University of Kent. Helen Smith, Hilary Brown and other colleagues provided an invaluable resource of information and advice.

Finally, I am indebted to those users and carers who in their various ways have highlighted for us the things that are important in providing services to people.

Introduction

THIS BOOK

Case management is an opportunity to take a bottom-up approach to planning and delivering services based upon the needs and strengths of individual users. This view springs from the experience of working with the Early Intervention Service (EIS), an inner London community mental heath team practising case management. Many of my colleagues there were as battle-scarred and disillusioned as I over some of the more negative experiences of work in mental health. In particular, we had all witnessed the raw deal that people with mental health problems receive from services. Working with the EIS showed me that case management can help to remedy many of the problems that we had all encountered. Although far from perfect, the EIS provides a worked example throughout the book.

The book is in three parts. Part One places case management in context by describing problems with service delivery for people with severe and long-term mental health problems and the potential for solving them through case management (Chapter 1); examining the relevant social policy (Chapter 2); looking at examples of case management in practice (Chapter 3); and considering organizational frameworks for case management (Chapter 4). Part Two focuses on the day-to-day practice of case management (Chapters 5 to 8). Part Three examines team working as a way of achieving high-quality case management. It describes the requirements for effective team working (Chapter 9); the management of teams (Chapter 10); and the development of high-quality services through innovation, training, and the development and monitoring of quality standards (Chapter 11).

The inclusion of guidelines on practice and organizational and social policy issues in a single volume reflects a trend embodied in case management itself. The devolution of responsibility to direct-care staff underlines their need to understand the organizational and political context in which they work. Mental health is inescapably a social and political issue reflecting radical social inequalities (Townsend and Davidson, 1982; Warner, 1985). Where workers are more aware and less passive within service systems, they are in a better position to safeguard the rights of users.

Certain assumptions and beliefs underpin the book. It assumes the reader is a practitioner or planner working in a mental health team or aiming to develop or join such a service in future. It also assumes the reader is committed to the provision of comprehensive, high-quality services to people with severe and long-term mental health problems. At risk of sounding hackneyed, it is also written with a firm belief in the tremendous social and societal importance of the work of mental health workers, and a recognition that their needs are frequently neglected in writings on service development.

SOME POINTS ABOUT LANGUAGE

There is a move towards adopting the phrase 'care management' in preference to 'case management', since 'care' is what service providers do (Department of Health, 1990, Social Services Inspectorate, 1991). Aside from the obvious need to qualify that assumption, the phrase 'care management' is avoided here because it obscures the central feature of this approach: a focus on the needs and strengths of individual users. Case management involves assessing and meeting users' needs rather than managing service provision ('care') *per se*. Indeed, in the past the word 'care' has been synonymous with passive users and powerful providers. Putting a dependent or troublesome relative 'into care' suggests banishment from everyday life. Although the word 'case' has unfortunate medical overtones and users have stressed that they are not cases to be managed; the phrase does emphasize the individual focus of case management that is perhaps its only wholly unequivocal defining characteristic. It is also more widely understood internationally. The term 'care management' is more logically reserved for the management of case management and provider agencies at a higher management tier (Challis, 1990).

Finding an appropriate word for the recipients of case management is problematic. In the absence of a better, widely understood alternative, the word 'user' will denote both people using services and those identified as being in need of assistance. The word 'client' is used where 'user' creates ambiguity. The word 'carer' refers only to the unpaid variety and includes partners, family and friends.

The 1990s began with a radical re-think in health and social service provision in Britain and a new, unfamiliar language. The term 'service providers' refers to those organizations that provide a service to users. Purchasing (or commissioning) agencies (e.g. district health authorities or local authorities) buy services from providers on a contractual basis. The 'independent sector' encompasses private, voluntary, charitable and not-for-profit agencies and may also be involved in both purchasing and providing.

Finally, this book is about people with severe and long-term mental health problems but does not refer to 'mental illness'. This does not reflect an anti-psychiatry stance or a denial of those phenomena associated with mental disorder that may have a biological basis (such as delusional thinking or auditory hallucinations). However, when looking at mental health issues in context, the term 'mental illness' obscures the social origins of severe and long-term distress and leads us to infer that problems lie in people's heads. A more comprehensive model is needed.

A MODEL FOR MENTAL HEALTH PROBLEMS

A stress-vulnerability model of mental health problems is assumed throughout the book. This model, shown in Figure 1, suggests that episodes of mental disorder or distress occur as a result of stress, enduring vulnerability, and coping difficulties.

Stress results from traumatic 'life events' such as bereave-

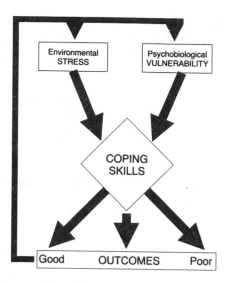

Figure 1 The stress-vulnerability model of mental health problems.

ment, separation and abuse, and more insidious, long-term experiences such as poor relationships or inadequate housing. **Vulnerability** is determined by genetic or biological factors and refers to enduring physical problems resulting in difficulties in areas such as processing information, focusing attention or managing levels of arousal. **Coping** refers to the way individuals respond to those aspects of their environment that challenge their well-being. Difficulty in coping arises from the interaction between vulnerability factors, stress factors and the absence of acquired skills or strategies to deal with stress. Those skills and strategies are determined by an internal model of the environment which is itself shaped by previous learning and experience. For example, failure to cope in the past with a particular challenge (e.g. job seeking) may give rise to an internal model of that situation as frightening and beyond the individual's self-perceived ability.

Originally, stress-vulnerability models suggested little more than the existence of a continuum of biologically determined vulnerability to mental disorder interacting with stress to produce psychotic episodes (Zubin and Spring, 1977). Subsequently, observations from various areas of research (such as that on information processing, social competence, life events and expressed emotion) were drawn into a coherent explanatory framework which highlighted the way difficulty coping and poor outcomes feed back to increase vulnerability (Nuechterlein and Dawson, 1984). For example:

> James was a young man who had been diagnosed as schizo-phrenic (among very many other things) and was frequently admitted to the local psychiatric unit. He appeared to have great difficulty understanding the things people were saying to him and was unable to express an opinion or rouse him-self to do anything. These were assumed to reflect vulner-ability factors.
>
> At home he was the object of very high levels of criticism from his father who regarded his son as a malingerer and constantly urged him to get a job. James seemed to experi-ence considerable stress as a result of his father's behaviour.
>
> James was unable to remedy the situation through seek-ing a job or talking to his family about his difficulties. The outcome was that he became disturbed, acted aggressively towards his mother and began routinely urinating in the corner. This attracted further criticism from his father lead-ing to an upward spiral of conflict and eventual admission to hospital. This was a regular and reliable sequence of events.

Apportioning aspects of James's behaviour to stress or vulnerability factors is not clear-cut. His initial apathy may not have reflected vulnerability factors but a sense of despair over ever fulfilling his father's expectations. However, stress-vulnerability models are helpful in giving us a way of under-standing how people get stuck in no-change situations leading to long-term mental health problems. They also help to avoid the rather sterile debate about whether, for example, people diagnosed as schizophrenic are experiencing predominantly biological or environmental problems. Most importantly, stress-vulnerability models indicate where services can usefully intervene to help people with mental health problems. For example, skills training promotes coping; crisis services help deal with adverse reactions to stress; environmental changes or work with families help prevent stresses reaching crisis point; and medication moderates the biological contribution to vulnerability. Stress-vulnerability models suggest ways in which services *could* intervene but say nothing about *why* they operate in the way they do. The role of services as an agent for the social control of deviance and the attendant potential for abuse should not be neglected. However, a stress-vulnerability approach points us in the right direction by highlighting the need to maintain a broad view of the diversity of demands that users can legitimately make of mental health services if we are serious about developing high-quality services.

Part One

Case Management in Context

Chapter 1

Why case management?

WHAT IS CASE MANAGEMENT?

The development of a relevant service will be influenced by the needs of users and local circumstances. As a result, there are many different approaches to the organization and practice of case management. The definition of case management given here is therefore a minimal one. It assumes that other features, which some authors might consider defining characteristics, will be encompassed according to their merits.

Case management is a way of tailoring help to meet individual need through placing the responsibility for assessment and service coordination with one individual worker or team.

The core tasks of case management are:

1. Assessment. The case manager achieves a clear picture of an individual's needs and strengths;
2. Planning. On the basis of the assessment the case manager leads the development of a plan that contains clearly specified outcomes and is easy to refer to;
3. Implementation. The plan is to be put into action with the involvement of users, their supportive personal contacts, and whatever range of agencies best meet the various needs identified;
4. Monitoring. Progress, or lack of it, towards specified objectives is systematically monitored and recorded;
5. Reviewing. The outcomes of the planned intervention are evaluated with the involvement of everyone connected with the work. As this evaluation requires a fresh examination of the needs and strengths of the individual user, review can be seen as a re-assessment, and thus the cycle repeats.

These tasks are not a series of separate events. They run in parallel and are inextricable. Through maintaining on-going relationships with users, case managers continuously assess emerging needs and strengths, plan and intervene to achieve the best fit of provision, and monitor to ensure desired outcomes are being achieved. Case management should never be a 'hit and run' exercise.

Depending upon the particular model of case management adopted, case managers may also identify and assist people through outreach work, act as therapist or counsellor, perform an advocate role, or act as a broker for other helping agencies. The latter may include managing a budget to buy services on behalf of individual users. This aspect has been afforded great importance in British case management models. More contentiously, case managers may also carry responsibility for rationing services.

OBSTACLES TO HIGH QUALITY CARE

Systems for providing help to people with severe and long-term mental health problems are prone to a number of problems and deficiencies. These include a mismatch between need and services provided, fragmented and discontinuous service provision, neglect of those most in need of services, neglect of informal carers, and problems of accountability.

Mismatch between user need and service provision

The 1980s witnessed a burgeoning user movement arising from dissatisfaction with mental health service provision (Sayce, 1990; Campbell, 1990). Becoming a user of services is often associated with the removal of power and choice. Indeed, some reject the term 'user' in favour of 'recipient' as this better conveys a sense of falling prey to mental health services (Campbell, 1990). Although there are clear divisions over models for understanding mental disorder among users and carers, they are united in demanding greater control over services and more attention to the range and long-term nature of the difficulties they are experiencing.

The obvious cause of insufficiency of service provision is absolute lack of resources. Although this is undeniable, it is not a sufficient explanation. In the relatively well-served area of Camberwell, London, Brewin *et al.* (1988) estimated that among people attending psychiatric services there was one unmet need for every five needs met. Just over a half had at least one unmet need for assessment or clinical intervention. Looking more closely at the pattern of interventions, those most frequently overprovided were neuroleptic, anticholinergic, antidepressant and anxiolytic drugs. Underprovision was most evident in psychological and educational interventions, including advice on coping and skills training. These findings, based upon clinical assessment and researchers rating the importance of need, coincide with concern about the overuse of drugs expressed by users. A survey of 500 users found 60% had been given treatments they did not want. They expressed concern over lack of choice and severity of side effects, with 90% seeing their problems as predominantly personal or social rather than medical (MIND/Roehampton Institute, 1990). Through neglecting social factors, service provision can exacerbate the problems that give rise to mental health service needs in the first place. People from black and ethnic communities may encounter racial abuse, misunderstanding, language barriers and a resulting readiness on the part of services to compulsorily hospitalize, diagnose and medicate them (Fernando, 1988; Francis *et al.*, 1989). Women are also at increased risk of mental distress due to social factors (Brown and Harris, 1978) and there is a greater tendency to perceive women as deviant within a male-dominated society (Showalter, 1987).

Services have also been guilty of a neglect of basic material needs. A study of three psychiatric units in inner London found that, of 215 consecutive admissions, 27% were homeless and 28% continued to be homeless at discharge (Hatch and Nissel, 1989). Although some of the latter were referred to homeless person units where they may conceivably have obtained permanent accommodation, the finding is an indictment of the way hospital services neglect basic material needs. One consistent finding of research on residential settings is that characteristics of the environment are more predictive of outcome than characteristics of the residents (Anthony and

Blanch, 1989). No wonder, then, that around three-quarters of all psychiatric hospital admissions are re-admissions (Office of Health Economics, 1989). Provision of decent accommodation is the cornerstone of a viable service system.

Scheff (1975) described the notion that enduring change in people can be achieved without consideration of their social and physical environment as the 'psychological fallacy'. Although this achieves its apogee in the practice of traditional analytical psychotherapy and biological psychiatry, therapists from other backgrounds are also guilty of neglecting environmental factors (Masson, 1988). In long-term institutional care, the opposite problem may occur where practical issues may be dealt with but psychological needs are neglected.

Need can be considered in terms of complexity and extensiveness (Challis and Davies, 1986). People present problems that are complicated and require a wide range of different forms of input over long periods of time. Multidisciplinary working in teams attempts to address the sheer diversity of needs that people present. In practice, however, teams often replicate the practice of acute admission facilities in over-emphasizing what is going on in someone's head at the expense of whether they have adequate accommodation, occupation, social and leisure opportunities (Echlin, 1988).

Too often, an assessment is of eligibility for a particular service rather than an independent evaluation of need (Goldberg and Connelly, 1982). This leads to provision based upon uniform packages (e.g. a fortnightly appointment with a community mental health nurse, occupational therapy, 'day hospital treatment'). Even within these traditional categories, Hatch and Nissel's (1989) survey identified considerable mismatch between need and provision. Glennerster et al. (1983) argued that this mismatch arises from the widespread application of 'gross planning methodologies': grouping users into categories that mask individual variation, focusing on disabilities rather than abilities, defining need in terms of existing services rather than in terms of what services should be achieving for people, and failing to incorporate the experience of staff involved in service delivery in the planning process.

High-quality services should aim to offer comprehensive assistance based upon a genuine assessment of need from the user's perspective. They should avoid overcomplicating already complex issues while being sophisticated enough to investigate the full breadth of individual need and intervene at an early stage before problems become compounded or exacerbated. This tall order requires an accessible, comprehensive and in-depth assessment and a high degree of service flexibility.

Fragmented and discontinuous services

Services for people with mental health problems are riddled with cracks for them to fall through: when trying to reach hospital care, at discharge, in between statutory and independent agencies, and even between members of the same mental health team. Services are planned on the basis of location (e.g. hospital, community, residential care), age group (e.g. 'the elderly'), profession (e.g. psychologist, nurse, doctor), groupings of disabilities (e.g 'challenging behaviours'), and time of day (e.g. 'day care') with inadequate coordination of the various service options available or efforts to smooth the transition from one to another. For example, since the Seebohm reorganization, British social services have been organized so that workers providing residential care and those providing services to people in their homes (e.g. home helps) operate in almost totally separate spheres. They often report to separate managerial hierarchies, meeting at around assistant director of social services level; organizationally a long way from the user and discouraging coordinated delivery of these two alternative forms of care.

Services are often shaped by long-standing work roles, expectations and practices. For example, a field social worker may on the basis of their assessment decide that a user requires home help. The home help becomes the worker with most direct contact with the user but is not responsible for assessment and review. Managers of home helps devote their energies to managing a budget and a group of staff, rather than reviewing need. As a result the user continues to receive the same uniform package of care until it deviates so far from their changing needs that a crisis is encountered. A similar and common problem concerns people who lose contact with services after discharge from hospital, and subsequently become distressed. One study followed users a year after discharge from hospital and found only 17% fulfilled discharge plans as expected (Caton, 1981). High drop-out is far from unusual (Huxley, 1990). Sometimes users do not need to lose contact with services for this to happen since poor coordination and communication between agencies may be damaging enough. The agency involved (for example, a hostel or a family) may have such poor support from specialist workers (such as psychiatrists) that a crisis is reached before an adequate assessment of the situation is achieved.

Neglect of those most in need

People with severe, long-term and complicated needs are often a surprisingly low priority for services. An assessment of service needs among the population of Sacramento, California, indicated that the 'acting-out and recidivist' population had 40% more problems with medication and 300% more behaviour problems than the population as a whole. Despite this they received less services than 'easier to handle' users, 50–60% less monitoring of medication and 20% less activity aimed at linking them with outside programmes (Leavitt, 1983). The tendency has been for services to err towards people presenting with minor mental health problems. Although there are some important exceptions, the community mental health movement in the US failed to offer a comprehensive service that would allow closure or a significant drop in bed numbers at state hospitals (Dowell and Ciarlo, 1983).

In Britain, Weller (1989) asserts that, 'The planning of future mental health care . . . increasingly reflects the influence of [a] distressed but generally articulate middle-class group of psychotherapeutic sophisticates, who are preoccupied with the discomforts of the worried well and are living in a cosy symbiotic relationship with psychotherapists' (p. 251). Despite handsome princes materializing in the form of calls to prioritize services for people with severe and long-term disabilities (e.g. Cmnd 6233, 1975; House of Commons Social Services Committee, 1985) they remain under-staffed and under-resourced. Devalued people are at risk of receiving devalued services from other devalued people (Brown and Smith, 1989).

In the meantime, de-institutionalization is increasingly being linked with the criminalization of mental health, and growing numbers of people with mental health problems residing in prison or on the streets (Weller, 1989). Many homeless people have significant mental health problems and this is often exacerbated by alcohol or drug dependence (Fischer and Breakley, 1986). A sample of men coming to a Salvation Army hostel showed that 31% would be diagnosed schizophrenic and that more than half were not in contact with psychiatric services (Timms and Fry, 1989). While some are simply out of touch with services, others may be actively avoiding them because of their past experiences (Satchell, 1988).

Weller (1989) calls for a halt to hospital closures and a return to hospital-based care with psychiatry firmly in the driving seat. A similar trend has been observed in the US and is most apparent in the drive to clear the streets of people who the general public may find unpleasant or distressing (Onyett, 1991a). We should not be so quick to abandon community care in Britain, particularly as research emerges indicating positive outcomes, good quality of life, a preference among users and lower costs compared with hospital care, even for the most difficult to serve users (Knapp *et al.*, 1990, 1991).

Targeting the most dependent and difficult to serve people has been a feature of successful demonstration projects (Bachrach, 1980). Such services need to be valued enough to attract high-calibre workers, accessible to vulnerable people, and in the case of some client groups, positively assertive in engaging them.

Neglect of informal carers

Working in mental health is tough. It has been said that anyone entering into it should be prepared for an experience that is more like 'a raid on Entebbe than an afternoon at the Epcot Centre' (Provencal, 1987). However, living with mental health problems is harder still. The relatives of someone with mental health problems face a wearisome task that may seem to offer little reward and less status.

Rapid closure of long-stay hospitals, inadequate funding of alternatives, and lack of vision when designing services all contribute to greater demand on families and services. Government policy has tended to legitimize the assumption that it is normal for dependent people to be cared for by their (usually female) relatives. Indeed, services are often withheld on the basis that the user has family support. Hudson (1987) argues that in so doing, services are operating a policy which penalizes those families willing to retain the primary support function, rather than complementing existing informal networks. The 'hidden item on the policy agenda' may be to exploit unpaid care by families in order to reduce competition for resources as more people seek independent lives in the community (Hudson, 1987; Goodwin, 1989). Only about 15% of families in the UK conform to the stereotypical family configuration for supporting dependent relatives: an able-bodied woman at home supported by an employed husband. Social and geographical mobility has meant smaller family sizes and more dispersed family structures, meaning fewer informal carers. Whether services intervene depends on the prevailing ideology regarding welfarism and sexism. In the meantime, the reality for carers is extreme restrictions on their social and leisure activities, financial problems and very little support or advice from helping agencies (Fadden *et al.*, 1987).

This neglect is partly due to the professionals' tendency to emphasize what is assumed to be happening in people's heads rather than users' social contexts, and 'hit and run' assessments that omit any enquiry into domestic life and family relationships. Indeed, service providers may inadvertently exacerbate family problems by providing assistance inappropriately or too late, usurping rather than complementing the care of families, and even acting as an incentive for them to give up (Moroney, 1976). Services should support rather than interfere with relationships within families or partnerships, except in those few instances when it is in the user's interests that services should intervene. Carers are an invaluable source of knowledge, skill and practical assistance maintained over periods during which many service providers may have come and gone.

Problems of accountability

There is often considerable confusion and local variation in the devolution and allocation of responsibility and accountability. **Responsibility** is here defined as the tasks that are legitimately demanded of an agency or worker. **Accountability** describes to whom the agency or worker must report and receive sanction with regard to these tasks. The closeness of the weave of 'safety nets' for people trying to get help for mental health problems is determined by these factors and the way they operate within and between agencies.

Workers within agencies are responsible for providing or coordinating care. However, as described above, decisions about resource allocation for service delivery are often made some way from individuals assessing need. Workers find themselves constrained from above with only a limited set of responses available and few opportunities for creative problem-solving. A split can emerge between clinical responsibility for providing adequate care and managerial responsibility for managing resources. This division is exacerbated where lines of accountability for clinical work run up through professional line management hierarchies that have little connection with the resource-managing hierarchy.

Team working provides its own problems. Role-blurring causes workers to question, or have questioned, their unique contribution to the team: their particular responsibilities. This is all the more difficult to resolve if the aims and functions of the team as a whole are unclear. Issues of accountability may also be disabling. Is the worker accountable to their line manager, the team or the team leader, and for what aspects of their work? Occasionally, psychiatrists within teams confuse medical responsibility with the calamitous notion of 'ultimate clinical responsibility,' whereby other team members are accountable to doctors who can over-ride their decisions (Chapter 9).

A balance needs to be struck between individual freedom to exercise clinical skills and the monitoring of case-work, such that quality is maintained and the welfare of the user is ensured. The ideal has been described as 'protection with autonomy' (Stevenson and Parsloe, 1978). This requires information for managers on case load, working practice, use of resources and demand for services, and highlights the centrality of outcome measures of quality in informing service development. Greater autonomy also demands a corresponding increase in support, supervision and training.

At inter-agency level, problems of agency responsibility are encountered. Amidst a paucity of resources and a desire to cut or displace costs, salient user characteristics become universal exclusion criteria ('We don't take people with drink problems, drug problems, incontinence, wheelchairs, pets, in crisis, or on a Friday afternoon'). If an agency cannot be held to account for failing to provide a service to a particular group, such as single homeless people, then the problem is unresolvable. The respective responsibilities of the various service providers involved in providing assistance to people with mental health problems must be clearly specified. This is cited as a driving force behind British governmental social policy initiatives for the 1990s, and in particular the introduction of a mixed economy of care and the attendant contracting culture.

TOWARDS A COMPREHENSIVE MENTAL HEALTH SERVICE

So what is required of a comprehensive mental health service? Developing Individual Services in the Community (DISC) (Smith, 1990a) is an approach to service planning based upon service functions. By focusing on what services should be achieving for people, DISC represents a radical departure from the fragmented approach described above. Its starting point is to consider what help people need. You might like to take some time to consider this yourself before examining Figure 1.1 where some of needs people present are shown.

Looking at these needs, DISC draws out the essential service functions shown in Figure 1.2: case management, identification, maintenance, growth and development, and crisis stabilization. Case management has implications for the other functions and so will be considered separately.

Identification

Mental health services need to identify people with needs and be fully accessible to them. This includes being physically easy to reach through serving a local community, operating an open-door or drop-in facility, doing outreach work, actively publicizing the service, or simply being easy to find. It also means not further stigmatizing or devaluing people who use the service. This involves being acceptable and relevant to the local community by reflecting its ethnic and cultural values. In order to think ahead and remain relevant, the service must plan not only for people already receiving help but also for those not in contact with services. There may be important reasons why they have not perceived the service as being of value to them.

Maintenance

Mental health is inescapably a social and political issue. Poor mental health is associated with social deprivation, poor housing, unemployment and discrimination. In order to reduce the effects of stress and vulnerability, a comprehensive service must attend to the essentials for maintaining basic well-being. This includes secure and stable accommodation, adequate income, meaningful occupation and access to general health care.

Growth and development

People often encounter difficulties because of a lack of personal and inter-personal skills. As described earlier, the inability to use effective coping skills can exacerbate the effects of stress and vulnerability. Such skills may include relating to people, participating in enjoyable activities, cooking, shopping, or dealing with the normal trials of life such as failure, rejection, aggression, frustration, or falling in love. This is particularly true if individuals have been living for much of their life in long-term institutions. Mental health services need to help users develop or resurrect these skills. This could take the form of intensive counselling, a programme of training or a helpful pointer in the direction of opportunities for new learning.

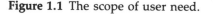

I NEED HELP WITH...

..emotional problems
..learning new skills
..getting though a crisis
..protection from abuse
..making and keeping friends
..getting and holding down a job
..finding somewhere pleasant to live
....getting a reasonable income
..improving my appearance or social manner
..coping with crazy thoughts and feelings
..finding opportunities for personal development
..finding something meaningful
to do during the day
..getting someone to speak on
my behalf if necessary
..finding someone who understands
my background and culture
..learning to relax
..getting over personal loss
..using public transport
..communicating with my family
..finding my way to services
..keeping going on anything
..saying when I need help

Figure 1.1 The scope of user need.

Identification

Crisis
stabilization

Maintenance

Case
management

Growth and
development

Figure 1.2 DISC service functions.

It is important that users decide for themselves what it is to 'cope' effectively. All therapies risk imposing alien value systems on individuals and of legitimizing existing social inequalities. Bell (1989) cites the example of an eminent cognitive therapist who described how resuming housework was part of his measure of 'positive outcome' for women being treated for depression.

Crisis stabilization

Many people come into contact with services through having encountered a crisis in their lives. The outcome of stressful events for individuals depends on the interaction between their vulnerability and their resources for coping, as described previously. Common triggers include bereavement, abuse, separation and homelessness.

An individual's reaction to crisis may create a dangerous situation for them and the people near them. They may become very disturbed and distressed, requiring immediate help so that they can restore their normal equilibrium as soon as possible. The ideal is to provide help where and when the crisis occurs. This is more likely to help the individual cope with a similar crisis in future. Often, however, the intervention is too late or the individual is temporarily unable to learn new skills and they need to be taken out of the situation. This may mean an admission to hospital which can severely disrupt supportive social networks, often to an irreparable degree (Lipton *et al.*, 1981). Other, less stigmatizing forms of 'asylum' may be more appropriate, particularly if they emphasize the involvement of people known and valued by the individual experiencing crisis (House of Commons Social Services Committee, 1990b). Crises demand a response that is flexible, immediate and in context.

THE POTENTIAL ADVANTAGES OF CASE MANAGEMENT

We have seen that a comprehensive service should aim to be relevant to a broad range of individual needs. In order to achieve this the service should be accessible, continuous, coordinated and flexible. It also needs to take as its starting point a thorough and unblinkered assessment of need. Through achieving these ends by making the best use of the resources available to it, such a service will also be cost-effective. The following begins to explore the potential for achieving these advantages.

Accessibility

From the outside, mental health service systems can present an intimidating array of providers, models of provision, and approaches to practice. The complexity often baffles not only users and carers, but other providers as well. Assigning case management responsibility to a named individual clearly specifies who to contact for help. Moreover, case managers can be given the job of assertively taking help to those who find it difficult to become involved in mental health services or are reluctant to do so because of negative expectations.

Continuity

Long-term mental health problems are typically episodic in nature. An individual may be coping well for long periods and then reach a point when their need for support increases drastically. Continuous, accessible contact with a named worker allows early intervention to prevent problems getting out of hand. Discharge from a long-stay hospital, seeking asylum in crisis, moving to a new home or getting a job can all be difficult times. During such periods it may be crucial for the user and their carers to find immediate support from a known and trusted individual, and for other agencies to be able to draw on the depth and breadth of knowledge that the case manager can offer in order to manage change most effectively.

Coordination

As we have seen, a comprehensive service aims to meet a wide spectrum of needs. It is not the job of the case manager to meet those needs personally; it *is* their job to see they are met. The case manager is responsible for ensuring that comprehensive assessment, monitoring and review of need is achieved, and that efforts are made to activate the services and other forms of help required. The job of the case manager is to coordinate the input of other workers or agencies in the task of achieving a high-quality service for individuals. Placing responsibility for coordinating assessment and service provision in the same place enables outcomes to be continually monitored.

Flexibility

Tailoring services to need means avoiding the monolithic nature of traditional service provision whereby services are provided in uniform immutable blocks. Goffman's (1961) seminal *Asylums* highlighted the ways in which 'total institutions' damage people by placing them in environments geared towards meeting the needs of service providers and society, rather than people with needs. Work on the lives of people with learning difficulties in residential care and studies of the interactions between staff and users in local authority day centres have pointed to the positive effects of user-centred management and organization (King *et al.*, 1971; Shepherd and Richardson, 1979).

User-centred approaches to the planning of care are still very far from universally practised within mental health, although the situation is somewhat better in services for people with learning difficulties (Blunden *et al.*, 1987). Case management provides on-going assessment and review in concert with continuous modification of service inputs to produce the best possible outcome for users. In acting as an agent for linking users to supportive services, case managers are able to be very specific about the service provided. Some models of case management increase this flexibility by providing case managers with a budget for buying in services (Challis and Davies, 1986).

Efficiency

Case management has created an unusual alliance between front-line staff and senior managers (Renshaw *et al.*, 1988). Practitioners advocating the principles of normalization applaud the tailoring of service provision to individual need rather than fitting people into pre-existing services (Brown and Smith, 1991). Managers may value the same features but for economic reasons. Inevitably, resources for service delivery are finite. For this reason, conscientious purchasers and providers must consider the best use of available resources. This involves examining service efficiency. A service is efficient when it provides enough resources to meet need effectively, and curtails or withholds provision when it is unnecessary. For example, long-stay institutions are effective in providing people with meals, and a cleaning and laundry service. They are, however, inefficient inasmuch as most people, at least when they go in, may not require such services but might have other needs such as training in specific skills or simply stimulating and supportive human contact. Inefficiency tends to be associated with uniform packages of care.

Efficiency is not just about saving money. Indeed, efficiency may be associated with increased costs if, as a result of efficiency in identification, more people are found who need services provided (Intagliata, 1982). Challis and Davies (1986) have delineated different aspects of service efficiency:

Input mix efficiency

This is the extent to which a combination of service inputs addresses assessed needs and strengths. It is concerned with the way services are able to join together cooperatively to provide a flexible and coherent whole.

Technical efficiency

After a combination of inputs has been decided, the package must be monitored, reviewed and modified to maximize effectiveness. Indeed, the whole working practice of any agency should be constantly under this kind of scrutiny. Technical efficiency refers to the extent to which a service is effective in meeting specific goals. For example, if one service input is a clinical psychologist working with someone on their social skills in the hope that this will increase their use of local shops, this input will need to be monitored in order to examine whether it really is the best way of achieving that goal.

Horizontal target efficiency

Horizontal target efficiency describes the degree to which a service connects with all potential users in a locality. The aim is that everybody who could benefit from the service has access to it. In DISC terms this is efficiency in identification.

Vertical target efficiency

This describes the extent to which the service engages *only* those people that it was set up to serve. It requires unambiguous specification of the client group and gate-keeping to screen out people whose needs would be better met elsewhere.

Target efficiency is influenced by the context of the service. For example, a service that is part of a planned re-provision programme for people leaving a long-stay hospital will find it much easier to achieve horizontal target efficiency than a street agency serving homeless people with severe mental health problems. Similarly, a service that operates with a single point of entry where gate-keeping and screening can be carried out will find it easier to achieve vertical target efficiency.

Output efficiency

This is the extent to which a service has achieved its overall objectives given a specified level of resources.

The specific outcomes of case-management programmes are discussed in Chapter 3. It is clear, however, that case management can make it easier to answer the question, 'Is the composition and balance of service inputs meeting the user's needs?'. An emphasis on on-going assessment and review, combined with clear specification of the target client group, service objectives, resources deployed and the responsibility and accountability for work undertaken makes it easier to evaluate service provision, feed the information into an overall assessment of need, and thereby influence policy. Figure 1.3 illustrates this process. Service development should be an iterative process where planning and implementation are based upon an assessment of the needs of groups of people. Case management is itself a process for collecting information on the needs of users and the ways in which they are being met. On the basis of clear individual needs assessments, detailed service plans can be accurately costed, and alternatives weighed up in order to achieve the best constellation of provision. For this to

Figure 1.3 Case management as part of a planning cycle.

work it is absolutely crucial that clearly defined indicators and standards of quality are integral parts of any package. Case managers are well placed to monitor quality indicators, under- and overprovision, and barriers to efficient delivery. This information, if fed into a service review, informs the on-going assessment of the needs of the identified client group as a whole and the adequacy of current service provision.

Advantages for workers

A case manager is in the privileged position of being able to oversee a process that can materially improve someone's quality of life. This contrasts with traditional work roles where lower status workers enjoy less influence in decision-making with users while spending more time with them than any-one else. The very lowest status workers are usually carers.

Among paid staff, mental health nurses are a good example of an undervalued group who often find themselves merely executing the decisions of psychiatrists and psychologists even though they may have a far greater understanding and appreciation of the user's needs and desires (Lang, 1982).

The assumption of case management responsibility by direct-care staff is associated with increased autonomy. Where this is accompanied by adequate training, support, supervision and pay it may also increase staff status and morale. As long as people with severe and long-term mental health problems are valued enough for services to earnestly attempt to address their needs, the direct-care staff who work with them are more likely to be likewise valued. Case management may offer a vehicle for such developments.

CONCLUSIONS

Case management presents service providers with an opportunity to improve mental health service organization and delivery. It glues fragmented services together into a continuous and coherent whole through locating responsibility for assessment and coordination with one person or agency. By operating flexibly at a level close to the user, case management can circumvent some of the disadvantages of uniform blocks of service provision, allowing help to be closely tailored to the needs of individuals and their carers. Through placing greater responsibility with direct-care staff, services can become more mobile, allowing help to go to users rather than vice versa. The case manager offers an unambiguous point of contact for users, carers and referrers, allowing improved accessibility in times of crisis and generally permitting earlier intervention. Improved staff effectiveness and morale can be predicted as workers become involved in a holistic approach to people's problems of living. The clear specification of services delivered and the results, along with improved definition of responsibility and lines of accountability, provide an opportunity to collect information that is of practical value in reviewing service provision and developing efficient services over the longer term.

However, these advantages do not accrue automatically to a

service that designates workers as case managers. There are potential costs to both users and mental health workers that can only be minimized through careful consideration of the organizational context and practice of case management.

Chapter 2

The social policy context

THE ORIGINS OF CASE MANAGEMENT

American precedents

Case management is far from new to the US where it arose as an attempt to overcome the fragmentation of services that accompanied community-based care. In the 1950s mental health care was almost exclusively the job of large state-operated public hospitals. Despite the best intentions of the reforming movement that had established these hospitals, they had become a way of segregating devalued people in scandalous conditions.

It is widely believed that the introduction of the phenothiazines produced improvements in the symptomatic treatment of major mental disorder, thereby allowing the development of services for people with severe and long-term mental health problems outside institutions. However, contemporary commentators were unimpressed by these drugs and the reasons for the rapid reduction in hospital populations are actually much more complex (Warner, 1985, Goodwin, 1989).

The early 1960s saw increased pressure for community care from civil libertarians who had achieved some success in establishing the right to treatment in the least restrictive setting and other procedural safeguards for involuntary psychiatric patients. However, the 1960s were actually a period of trans-institutionalization rather than de-institutionalization. Many people were simply transferred from hospitals to nursing homes where conditions were often even worse. Between 1963 and 1969 the combined numbers of people in hospitals and nursing homes *increased* (Warner, 1985).

In 1963 the Community Mental Health Centres Act led to the creation of centrally-funded centres across the country aimed at serving people leaving psychiatric hospital. New national health insurance schemes for impoverished and older people introduced in 1965, and the Supplemental Security Income programme in 1974, provided financial incentives for state policy-makers to discharge people from hospital in order to transfer the cost of mental health services from state to federal government. Central funding of the community mental health centre (CMHC) programme was to be phased out as states assumed the greater burden of care. However, perhaps unsurprisingly, states were unwilling to fund services that they had little involvement in designing or implementing.

Federal and state funding became parallel and often conflicting systems (Mosher and Burti, 1989). Only 789 of the 2000 or so CMHCs planned ever materialized (Levine and Fleming, 1984) and those that did have been criticized for lacking clear service objectives and failing to serve people with severe and long-term mental health problems (Dowell and Ciarlo, 1983).

The CMHCs and the new funding arrangements did succeed in rapidly increasing the range and quantity of service providers. However, poor inter-agency collaboration and the absence of any coordination has resulted in a plethora of individual programmes providing specialized services to narrowly defined client groups. Navigating the system is almost impossible for people with multiple service needs whose ability to cope with problems of daily living is seriously impaired. The early 1970s saw an attempt to address this problem through National Institute of Mental Health (NIMH) projects designed to improve coordination at inter-organizational level. The projects incorporated the role of 'systems agent' or case manager who would coordinate services at the case level in order to provide continuity of care and a consistent relationship for users. Since 1974, NIMH has been encouraging states to develop 'community support systems' for people with severe and long-term mental health problems. These aim to offer a comprehensive system of service provision within which specific services can be tailored to individual need. Community support systems require ten essential functions or components (NIMH, 1977; Stroul, 1989):

1. Identification of the target population whether in hospitals or in the community, and outreach to offer appropriate services to those willing to participate.
2. Assistance in applying for entitlements.
3. Crisis stabilization in the least restrictive setting possible, with hospitalization available when other options are insufficient.
4. Psychosocial rehabilitation services, including but not limited to;
   (a) goal-orientated rehabilitation training in community living in natural settings wherever possible;
   (b) opportunities to improve employability;
   (c) appropriate living conditions in an atmosphere that encourages improvements in functioning;
   (d) opportunities to develop social skills, interests, and leisure time activities that promote a sense of community participation and worth.
5. Supportive services of indefinite duration, including supportive living and working arrangements, and other such services for as long as they are needed.
6. Medical and psychiatric care.
7. Support for families, friends and community members.
8. Involvement of concerned community members in planning and offering housing or work opportunities.
9. Protection of users' rights, both in hospitals and in the community.
10. Case management to ensure continuous availability of appropriate assistance.

The Accreditation Council for Psychiatric Facilities (1976) provided a comprehensive description of case management: 'Case management services are activities aimed at linking the service system to a consumer and at coordinating the various system components to achieve a successful outcome . . . Case management is essentially a problem-solving function designed to ensure continuity of service and to overcome systems rigidity, fragmented service, misutilization of certain facilities, and inaccessibility' (pp. 20–21). Further support for the need for case management was lent by the President's Commission on Mental Health (1978) which concluded that, 'Strategies focused solely on organizations are not enough. A human link is required. A case manager can provide this link and assist in assuring continuity of care and a coordinated program of services'. The commission went on to recommend that state mental health authorities develop a case management system for every geographical service area within the state.

The 1980s saw burgeoning case management systems with all 50 states receiving Community Support Programme grants. Features such as case management, psychosocial rehabilitation, and supported accommodation are becoming more available. However, residential alternatives to hospitalization, neuroleptic-free therapy for people diagnosed as psychotic, and the therapeutic importance of psychosocial interventions have not gained such acceptance. The enduring dominance of the medical profession has resulted in a continued disproportionate allocation of resources to in-patient care and an inadequate range of psychosocially-orientated community-based alternatives (Mosher and Burti, 1989).

British social policy to 1989

Whereas cost saving was the main impetus for de-institutionalization in the US, Warner's (1985) research suggests that it was the post-war demand for labour that provided the impetus for rehabilitative efforts in Britain and northern Europe. These changes in the labour market may also have influenced a philosophical shift towards greater optimism regarding the efficacy of social and environmental approaches to understanding and alleviating mental health problems. Further impetus towards community care was added by the physical deterioration of the Victorian institutions and an ideological shift away from psychiatry's custodial function towards an emphasis on treatment.

Although bed occupancy peaked in 1954, a more relevant statistic is the use of mental hospital beds as a proportion of the population (Goodwin, 1989). This brings the peak to 1930, about 25 years prior to the drug revolution that was the supposed catalyst to community care. Since this peak, patient throughput has increased with a corresponding decrease in average length of hospital stay. Although admissions have increased many times, the proportion of these that are first admissions has declined drastically, with 80% in 1930, 68% in 1950 and around 27% in the mid-1980s (*ibid.*). Thus although stays may be shorter, many people are caught in a 'revolving door' of repeated admissions to hospital.

Voluntary admission to mental hospitals was introduced by the Mental Treatment Act 1930. The Mental Health Act 1959 made admission less legalistic and promoted the development of community facilities. It described the powers of local authorities to provide services such as accommodation, occupation and training but did not provide extra resources for community care. The 1962 Hospital Plan for England and Wales stated that the number of psychiatric beds should be halved by the mid-1970s and advocated shorter hospital stays and the relocation of beds to local District General Hospital sites. This was reiterated with a White Paper (Cmnd 6233, 1975) which sought the expansion of the role of social services departments in residential, day care, domiciliary and social work support, better staffing and improved coordination between agencies.

A system for joint (health and local authority) finance was introduced to encourage integrated planning and service delivery. It aimed to promote social services initiatives of benefit to the National Health Service by providing health authorities with a fund to be spent on jointly planned projects. Wistow (1990) describes the disappointing outcome of this strategy. Problems stemmed partly from a lack of coordinated leadership from the centre with governmental disputes between different departments about policies for community care, local government finance and social security. Although the Social Services Inspectorate had a role in monitoring individual authorities, interventions tended to be in response to instances of potential or actual scandal, rather than a systematic and regular review of performance with reference to national policy objectives. Differences in management culture between health and local authorities, and absence of a symmetrical system for joint monitoring, and no shared accountability for the success or failure of inter-agency planning also provided obstacles to joint working (*ibid.*). The House of Commons Social Services Committee (1985) highlighted the failure of joint finance over the previous decade and advocated clearly defined care plans and the resources to ensure their implementation for everybody leaving psychiatric hospitals. It also rejected the idea that the provision of asylum was necessarily through large remote institutions.

The Audit Commission (1986) first described the deployment of case managers in detail. Their report drew attention to the short-fall in investment in services for people leaving hospital, and the immense variations among local authorities in their expenditure on services for people with mental health problems. They suggested that regional health authorities could frustrate moves towards community care because they had so little involvement with local authorities and were preoccupied with closing hospitals rather than considering alternative provision. The inadequacy of systems for monitoring the use of resources was also highlighted and they suggested a case management system with budgetary autonomy as a way of circumventing problems in inter-organizational collaboration. In 1986 the Government commissioned a review of community care policy led by Sir Roy Griffiths. It concluded that 'if community care means anything, it is that responsibility is placed as near to the individual and his carers as possible' and recommended that the case management role include strategic and financial responsibilities (Griffiths, 1988).

BRITISH GOVERNMENT POLICY FOR THE 1990s

In 1989 the British Government released the *Caring for People* white paper on community care (Cm 849, 1989) based on the Griffiths report. It followed close on the heels of a white paper on hospital and family practitioner services (Cm 555, 1989). Together, they represented a sea change in thinking about National Health Service and local authority provision and became law with the passing of the National Health Service and Community Care Act (1990). Their central argument lay in the putative advantages of applying market forces to the provision of health and social care founded on the assumption that competition increases efficiency and drives out incompetent and undesirable service provision. To create a market situation a split was created between those concerned with purchasing services on behalf of the local population, and those concerned with providing services via contracts. Emphasis was placed on strict costing of service provision to allow purchasing agencies to weigh up the benefits of a range of alternatives. For the first time family doctors had the opportunity to control their own budgets for purchasing services for their patients and hospitals could opt out of District Health Authority control in order to allow themselves more flexibility to compete effectively within the new marketplace for service provision.

Inter-agency collaboration in community care is the key to the success of these policy initiatives (House of Commons Social Services Committee, 1990a). The initiatives and ideas described above often involve attempts to overcome service fragmentation and promote coordinated and efficient pro-vision. The following discussion considers whether the *Caring for People* initiatives are liable to promote coordination or fragmentation of service provision. This has significant bearing on the central role allocated to case managers as assessors of need and coordinators of resources within this new context.

Case management

The objectives of case management as described in government policy guidance (Department of Health, 1990) were to:

1. meet individual care needs through the most effective use of resources;
2. restore and maintain independence by enabling people to live in the community wherever possible;
3. prevent or minimize the negative effects of disability, illness or mental distress in people of all ages;
4. achieve equal opportunities for all;
5. promote individual choice and self-determination and build on existing strengths and care resources, and
6. promote partnerships between users, carers and service providers in all sectors.

The three core processes of case management were des-cribed as:

1. assessment which includes the support needs of carers;
2. planning and agreeing preferred options for support with

the involvement of users, carers and other relevant agencies. Although the plans will necessarily be within existing resources, information on any preferred solutions that are unavailable must be fed into the planning process;

3. implementation, monitoring, review and revision. This last process stressed the continuous nature of case management and the constant adjustment of assistance provided to achieve the best possible outcomes for users and carers.

The guidance emphasized that case managers should not be involved in service provision themselves, or manage provider agencies. This was in order to avoid conflicts of interest when assessing need and monitoring the effects of service provision. The viability of this recommendation for people with mental health problems is discussed in Chapter four.

The care programme approach

The care programme approach was aimed to serve all psychiatric in-patients considered for discharge, and all new users involved with specialist psychiatric services from April 1991. It demands that arrangements for support outside hospital are made prior to discharge. Consultant psychiatrists and their colleagues must decide whether such support is feasible in view of the available resources. Health care needs must be regularly reviewed and arrangements made with local social services departments to ensure the assessment of social needs. A hospital-based keyworker may be responsible for ensuring all this takes place.

Although attention to assessment and planning prior to discharge has been applauded, a number of concerns have arisen over care programming. It places considerable power in the hands of hospital-based psychiatrists who may lack a comprehensive view of community-based opportunities and have an investment in refusing to discharge patients in order to maintain their traditional power-base in psychiatric hospitals (House of Commons Social Services Committee, 1990b; Sayce, 1990). As a result, de-institutionalization may be slowed down or even reversed. Evidence from MIND to the Social Services Committee (House of Commons Social Services Committee,

1990b) stated that, 'It is usually the users themselves, with their friends, family and workers based in the community (such as housing or social workers) who have the greatest clarity about the community situation' (para. 86). The subsequent policy guidelines recommended a multidisciplinary decision-making process and the involvement of users and their advocates (Department of Health, 1990). However, this assumes that those people who can lay claim to responsibility for co-ordinating assessment, such as consultant psychiatrists, case managers and family doctors, can agree how an individual service plan should be drawn up and who is responsible for what tasks. Policy guidance offered little practical help (Royal College of Psychiatrists, 1989; Department of Health, 1990). For example, they suggest that the keyworker role includes assertive outreach work aimed at re-engaging people who have lost touch with services; a role more suited to a community-based worker familiar with the local environment. White and Brooker (1990) predicted that the care programme approach may lead to a return to closer working relationships between psychiatrists and community psychiatric nurses; a trend that is likely to be resisted by a profession that has sought to establish autonomous practice in primary care, rather than remain as an arm of hospital-based psychiatric teams.

Much confusion surrounds the relationship of care programming to case management. Both share the same core tasks, stress the involvement of users and carers, are concerned with the coordinated assessment of health and social care needs, and have convergent client groups. It is difficult to justify separate systems for assessment, monitoring and review, particularly in view of the need to avoid bureaucratic procedures for accessing help (Onyett, 1991b).

It seems present government guidelines are unlikely to promote coordinated care based upon users' wishes and needs. This may account for the lack of evidence of systematic implementation of care programming despite stringent deadlines.

The 'specific grant for people with a mental illness'

A specific grant to local authorities for revenue funding of services for people with severe mental health problems was

established as part of the *Caring for People* initiatives. In order
to encourage joint planning, it was made payable only on the
basis of joint health and local authority initiatives, with regional health authorities responsible for triggering the grant.
This is clearly an urge towards the coordination of services but
a very small one as only limited funds are available, and local
authorities are required to contribute a substantial proportion.
The Social Services Committee (House of Commons Social
Services Committee, 1990b) also expressed concern over the
grant being primarily focused on health-dominated programmes as a result of the health authority's triggering role,
and suggested that local authorities consult with users and
voluntary organizations to provide a 'countervailing pressure to
the "medical model"' (para. 53). In addition, the absence of a
definition of 'severe' mental health problems is problematic
and the lack of attention to those people who are not in contact
with services yet have severe and disabling problems has been
lamented (House of Commons Social Services Committee,
1990b; Sayce, 1990).

The health and social care divide

Caring for People emphasized the distinction between health
and social care, without offering much guidance as to their respective definitions. One approach is to examine the elements
of provision and decide whether they are predominantly health
or social care. For example, there are calls for health authorities to be remunerated from local authority funds for any
residential care provided by health facilities and likewise local
authorities may be remunerated for any nursing care provided
in local authority premises.

However, at practice level health and social care may be
very difficult to separate. One provider recently commented
that the only difference between a health bath and a social bath
is that Dettol goes into one and bubble bath into the other! An
alternative is for health and local authorities to look at special-
ities by client group and decide on a lead agency. For example,
services for people with mental health problems may remain
within the purview of health authorities because of the traditional emphasis on medical practice. If these demarcations can

be successfully negotiated the health and social care divide may act as a way of achieving clarity about respective responsibilities between agencies, thereby improving coordination. If not, it may open up cracks in service provision as agencies engage in disputes over which aspects of care they are liable to pay for in attempts to divest themselves of costs. The ideal outcome is jointly agreed community care plans and a collaborative approach to assessing the needs of the local population. Given that planning is an iterative process, it seems likely that agencies that start together are more likely to stay together, particularly if they are able to share information and a vision of what the service as a whole should be achieving. The worst scenario is that the split remains unresolved at a senior level and workers, carers or users are left to decide pathways to support by default.

Multidisciplinary working

Caring for People emphasizes a multidisciplinary approach. Whether this achieves effective coordination depends upon the resolution of common problems with multidisciplinary working. Clarity over aims, priorities and definitions of team members' respective responsibilities and lines of accountability are needed. These conditions, combined with a single point of contact for users and carers and devolved responsibility for assessment and coordination, form the very basis of improved services through case management described in this book.

Resources

Caring for People deviated from Griffiths' (1988) recommendations by not introducing ring-fenced funding or a specific government minister for community care. Resources for community care come from a bewildering array of sources and the total allocation is difficult to determine. It is clear, however, that there has been a disproportionate allocation of resources to hospital-based care. Investment in hospital care for people with mental health problems decreased only 3% between 1978 and 1988, compared with 12% for people with learning difficulties. In 1988, local authorities contributed only 4% of total expenditure on services to people with severe and long-term mental health problems, compared with 38% for people with learning difficulties. This represents an increase of only 1% for mental health services since 1978, compared with 13% for service for people with learning difficulties (House of Commons Social Service Committee, 1990b). Resources continue to be concentrated in the one location that users do not want to occupy: the hospital (Knapp *et al.*, 1991; MIND/Roehampton Institute, 1990).

Caring for People made local authorities the lead agency for social care (as suggested by Griffiths) while promoting a mixed economy of service provision by providing incentives for local authorities to use independent sector provision rather than their own facilities. Case managers have the job of assessing users' needs for social care and making the best use of the new mixed economy. However, the transfer of funds to local authorities needed to implement these changes was delayed by the Government till 1993 in order to avoid politically damaging increases in poll tax. Even then, in the absence of ring-fencing, there are no guarantees that the money will be spent on people with severe and long-term mental health problems or learning difficulties.

A lack of resources almost inevitably leaves major gaps in service provision or exposes users to low-quality care. One way of regulating the demand on resources is to manipulate the eligibility criteria for access to the mental health system. There is a danger that this is a task which will be devolved to case managers.

Quality assurance in the internal market

The only way in which resource constraints can act as an urge towards coordination is if they promote the rational and efficient use of resources in the interests of positive outcomes for service users. This demands mechanisms for clear service specification and monitoring of provision. From 1991, regional health authorities and local authorities are expected to establish 'arm's length' inspection units to monitor and promote high-quality services in residential or other facilities provided by the local authority or the independent sector. In addition, complaints procedures will be established and procedures and eligibility criteria for assessment made public. These developments have all been welcomed. However, there is concern over the lack of independence of the monitoring system (Sayce, 1990). This is particularly important in view of the risk of purchasers pressurizing providers to lower standards in order to meet contracted case loads and stay within budget, and the possibility of purchasers simply declining to attend to quality indicators (East Anglian Regional Health Authority/Office for Public Management, 1990; Peck and Smith, 1990).

It has yet to be seen whether market forces really will create a new diversity of services attractive to users. Health and social services may take the opportunity to divest themselves of service provision by sale or contracting out to the independent sector. The commercial sector is likely to exploit the opportunity to develop residential or support services. Although this may increase diversity in the short term, the cut-and-thrust nature of the market may mean that one sector eventually comes to dominate while others withdraw, restricting choice and access to services. Also, the application of economic theory to mental health neglects the point that factors other than user choice determine use of services. Given the influence of social factors in determining the prevalence of mental distress and the ways in which services respond (Chapter 1), purchasers and providers will need to do much more than pay lip-service to equal opportunities issues, particularly given the potential for mental health services to be used for social control.

In the US, purchase of service and systems of public and private health insurance have determined service provision for a long time. Comparisons do not encourage optimism. In Massachusetts, contracting has resulted in lower wages leading to poor continuity of care and staff turnover of between 40% and 80% annually. In addition, services are of low quality and inadequately monitored, procedures are highly bureaucratic, user groups are marginalized and large private providers gain political power over public purchasers as they achieve monopoly status (Schlesinger, Dorwart and Pulice, 1986). The British should be doubly concerned. In Scandinavia and some American states, people have established an unequivocal right to service provision. No such rights exist in Britain.

LOOKING TO THE FUTURE

Although resting on excellent statements of principle, the
Caring for People proposals lack the clarity required to ensure
coordinated, high-quality care. The care programme approach
and the use of the specific grant are critical features that have
not been integrated with the proposals for case management.
A rational long-term solution to the problem of allocating
responsibility is to give case managers the task of coordinating
all assessment for mental health services regardless of whether
users are living in the community or leaving hospital. This
demands a radical shift of the traditional centre for mental
health care from the hospital to the community and requires
close liaison, perhaps in the form of joint assessment, with
hospital-based clinicians and family doctors. The House of
Commons Social Services Committee (1990b) recommended
that the specific grant be used to set up joint health and local
authority multidisciplinary teams to respond to emergencies.
This recommendation could be usefully expanded to encompass jointly-managed teams of case managers working with
users presenting in a variety of ways, including those discharged from hospital under the care programme approach.

The work of case managers in Britain will be shaped by the
ways in which agencies and their communities respond to the
demands of these policy changes. In a context of unrestrained
market forces, limited resources, and confused responsibility
and accountability at all levels, case managers may find themselves in quite disparate roles: as advocates for users, or
rationers of scarce provision. However, with effective joint
planning, adequate resourcing, appropriate stimulation of the
independent sector and a clear mandate to seek high-quality
provision, case managers may find themselves in an ideal
position to help achieve better services for users and carers.

Chapter 3

Learning from experience

This chapter describes projects that have employed a variety of case management models. All use the core tasks of assessment, planning, implementation, monitoring and review. However, beyond this differences emerge. For example, some employ an assertive approach working with people in their homes, some include a primary therapist role, some act as advocates for service users, some give case managers responsibility for managing a budget and some share responsibilities within a team. Given this huge diversity it is not possible to make definitive statements on the efficacy of case management and thus the right way to practise it (see Ryan *et al.* 1991; Thornicroft, 1991; Holloway, 1991; and Shepherd, 1990 for reviews). The ability to reproduce and generalize from model programmes is limited by the tendency for benefits to attend any new initiative, problems separating effects due to service design from those due to people running the service, and the need to view services holistically, including their organizational context and cultural base (Bachrach, 1980).

In order to determine the critical ingredients of a service, it is necessary to:

1. achieve a very clear and detailed definition of practice;
2. establish that the intended practice was implemented as planned;
3. specify clearly the target client group;
4. ensure that this group is in fact served;
5. determine the extent to which changes in practice correlated with changes in users' behaviour (e.g. their use of services);
6. determine which aspects of practice correlated with which aspects of users' behaviour, which in turn demands that
7. the effects of the service in question can be separated from

the effects of other changes in the users' environment (e.g. the behaviour of local services).

Establishing cause experimentally is a very demanding task requiring tightly controlled longitudinal evaluations of daunting complexity. Learning from the experience of other services means abandoning the search for model case management programmes to reproduce in favour of a more pragmatic approach. Some general conclusions can be drawn from research data, but it is also useful to draw from the experience of practitioners as to why their particular service was effective in their particular circumstances.

The services below have been grouped together according the client groups they are aiming to serve.

ALTERNATIVES TO HOSPITAL CARE FOR PEOPLE WITH SEVERE AND LONG-TERM MENTAL HEALTH PROBLEMS

Training in Community Living, Madison, USA

Although not the first study to look at alternatives to hospital treatment, the 'Training in Community Living' (TCL) programme in Madison, Wisconsin, had a very significant impact with replications in the US, Australia and Britain. The phrase 'case management' does not appear in descriptions of the service (Stein and Test, 1980). However, TCL contains many ideas that have subsequently formed the basis for 'assertive' case management, the practice of delivering services to people wherever they happen to be and actively working to maintain their involvement.

Work took place in the users' homes, neighbourhoods and places of work. The service offered comprehensive individual assessments and acted as a binding agent, drawing support together into a coherent whole. Each user had an individually tailored programme offering 24-hour, seven days a week coverage. Intensive effort was invested in finding jobs or sheltered work and TCL workers liaised with employers and supervisors to assist in on-the-job problem-solving. Attention was also given to teaching and assisting in activities of daily living, the constructive use of leisure time and the development of social skills. This particularly focused on users' strengths rather than aspects of pathology or disability. The service supported the involvement of families and other carers and if a user did not show up anywhere the TCL worker immediately visited at home in order to help overcome any obstacles that might prevent attendance. The service routinely medicated those users diagnosed as schizophrenic or manic depressive and carefully monitored their medical status.

To evaluate TCL, residents of Dane County aged between 18 and 62 presenting for hospital admission were randomly assigned to TCL or a control condition. (A control condition offers a comparison to the approach of interest.) The control offered 'progressive hospital treatment plus community after-care' providing high staff-to-user ratios and a wide range of services. Approximately half the sample of 130 were diagnosed as schizophrenic. Users had a mean of five previous admissions and 14.5 months in psychiatric institutions. Only 17% had never been in a psychiatric hospital. The mean age was 31, 55% were men and 73% were either single, separated or divorced.

Over the 14-month study period, only 12 of the 65 TCL users were admitted to hospital compared with 58 of the 65 control users. Re-admission rates in the first year were 6% for TCL versus 58% for the control. This did not result in increased use by the TCL users of other medical or penal institutions or supervised living situations in the community. They spent less time unemployed and more time in sheltered employment. TCL users were significantly more satisfied with their life situation although there was no significant difference on measures of the quality of their respective environments. There was no difference in the numbers of users prescribed medication but the TCL group complied significantly more with their medication regimes towards the latter phase of the experimental period. TCL users displayed fewer symptoms than the control users and presented no increased family or community burden in terms of frequency of arrests, suicidal gestures requiring medical attention or the use of the local emergency room (Test and Stein, 1980). Overall, the pro-gramme did incur additional costs and benefits but the benefits outweighed the costs even when considering purely economic (as opposed to social) factors (Weisbrod, Test and Stein, 1980). When the TCL programme stopped there was a rapid increase in symptomatology and the use of the hospital, and a decrease in compliance.

The Community Treatment Team, New South Wales, Australia

Hoult (1986) replicated the Madison project in Sydney, a city with ten times the population. The experimental condition entailed service from a Community Treatment Team (CTT) consisting of three psychiatric nurses, two social workers, a psychologist, an occupational therapist and a part-time psychiatrist. They offered the same range of services as the control but with a different approach to practice.

In this study an assertive and a 'passive-response' approach to case management were compared. Assertive case management emphasizes the active engagement of users and carers through work in community locations. The control condition offered standard hospital care and aftercare from a well-resourced service. Control group case managers only worked office hours and did not routinely visit users at home. CTT users were assessed at the hospital admissions office by the psychiatrist and one other member of the team. Where possible, relatives and other people in contact with the user were involved in individual service planning. These plans sometimes included rapid tranquillization using drugs. Threats of violence or suicide normally abated with 'support, firmness and medication'. Relatives were given information on the user's diagnosis and guidance on how to cope with symptoms and problematic behaviour. If the situation allowed, users were returned to their homes. Otherwise the CTT found alternative accommodation, such as a boarding house.

Initial involvement from the CTT worker was intensive. They would stay with the user for many hours until the situation became more settled, monitoring the effects of any medication given. The family could subsequently page the CTT worker if further problems occurred and this service was available around the clock. Initially, workers would attend frequently, sometimes taking the user out of the home situation in order to offer some respite to families. Hoult reports that during this phase a strong and enduring alliance was often created between workers, users and their families. For the majority of cases the worker faded their involvement as symptomatology lessened, although for others they continued in the manner of TCL, offering intensive training in coping skills *in situ*. Following contact with the CTT, the team remained responsible for future intervention and were contacted at an early stage if further problems occurred.

Over the one-year study period, the CTT users spent on average 8.4 days in hospital compared with 53.5 days among the controls. The CTT users had superior clinical outcomes and rated their care as significantly more satisfactory and helpful. Overall, relatives regarded the community treatment positively. Although community treatment was not as effective in reducing suicide threats or attempts, the mortality rate during and after the study was higher among those admitted to hospital. Separate analysis showed the same profile of results for those users with a diagnosis of schizophrenia (approximately half the sample). Looking at people presenting for admission for the first time, CTT users tended not to be admitted in the first place and were not subsequently re-admitted in the manner seen with the control condition. A cost analysis looking at direct and indirect, public and private costs found that the control condition was 26% more expensive than the CTT.

On the basis of these findings, Hoult recommended 'a personal case manager, who accepted responsibility for ensuring that the patient's needs were met and for coordinating with other agencies providing service' (p. 143). Other useful ingredients were:

1. intensive input at the beginning of involvement;
2. a willingness to involve others close to the user in assessment and planning;
3. consistent care by one team;
4. a willingness to assertively take services to the user and their family without being intrusive;
5. help with practical problems of daily living, including *in situ* training work;

Learning from experience

6. an easily accessible, mobile, rapidly responding 24-hour service, and
7. extensive and on-going service provision rather than a hit-and-run, time-limited approach.

Early Intervention Service, London

The EIS drew heavily on the CTT design and practice of case management. It serves an ethnically and socially diverse four square mile patch of inner London. There are a large number of homeless families living in bed-and-breakfast accommodation and, because of the presence of a major rail terminal, a large transient population.

The team aims to provide a service to those people experiencing a level of disturbance or distress that might otherwise result in hospital admission. In the first 30 months of operation, 550 referrals were accepted, the main sources being family doctors (34%), hospital-based social workers (11%), hospital-based doctors (8%), self-referrals (8%) and social services (8%). Rather than define its client group in diagnostic terms, the EIS accepted referrals on the basis of three criteria: severity of disturbance, whether the user was visibly crazy, and whether a community-based assessment was required. 51% of users had a psychiatric history with a mean of three admissions (ranging from one to 34) and a mean interval since first psychiatric contact of ten years. Adjustment disorder (14.4%) and paranoid schizophrenia (11%) were the most common diagnoses made by the EIS psychiatrist. The mean age was 36, 42% were male and 33% lived alone.

The team composition was as the CTT and all the clinicians took on case management responsibility in addition to their normal professional duties. Initial assessment was mainly performed in the user's home (53%), bed-and-breakfast hotels (12%), doctors' surgeries (12%), hospitals (8%) or hostels (7%). Assessment was carried out jointly with the referrer or another involved worker where possible (45%). Details on the EIS's operation and the case manager's role within the team are described in Chapter nine. To summarize, the initial assessment was taken back to a twice-weekly clinical review meeting for allocation to a case manager, or referral elsewhere if the case did not fulfil criteria. The work was usually carried out wherever the user resided (i.e. 64% in private homes, bed-and-breakfast hotels, or hospital) or in doctors' surgeries (12%). The case manager's role combined service coordinator, primary therapist and keyworker. They did not provide 24-hour cover.

The evaluation of the EIS took two forms: (1) a controlled study of the outcome of EIS provision compared with standard local psychiatric services for emergency referrals coming via an accident and emergency department or a psychiatric unit-based duty social work team (Merson *et al.*, 1991), and (2) an on-going description of the users of the service and the way in which the service operated (Onyett *et al.*, 1990).

At three months follow-up, the study of emergency referrals found significantly reduced length of hospital stays in the EIS group (1.2 vs. 9.3 days, p < 0.01) and increased user satisfaction (p < 0.001). A separate analysis revealed that the significant advantage for hospital stay was restricted to people diagnosed as schizophrenic. There was no difference on ratings of symptomatology and social functioning although both conditions achieved significant improvements over time.

The descriptive evaluation included a referrers' feedback survey which indicated a positive view of the EIS on all significant findings. The EIS policy of joint work was the most highly valued feature, followed by the accessibility and community location of the service. The least approval was for the appropriateness of the service for typical clients of the referrer, suggesting that there was considerable selection taking place before making referrals.

The Daily Living Programme, Camberwell, London

The Daily Living Programme (DLP) offered a problem-orientated case management approach to people living at home, and compared this to standard hospital-based care for people presenting for admission using a randomized control design. The aims and exclusion criteria were as the Madison and New South Wales studies. The team comprised seven nurses, a psychiatrist, a social worker, an occupational therapist and a coordinator. The DLP employed a keyworker system in which individual workers designed individualized programmes and coordinated resources for users. The project was linked with an emergency clinic allowing assessment for the project and access for users at all hours of the day. The support of the emergency clinic also allowed the project access to beds under the control of the DLP's psychiatrist.

Assessments took place at the first point of contact and were carried out by two team members, one of whom was the psychiatrist, senior nurse or charge nurse. Users were assessed at either the emergency clinic or their own home. Like the CTT, the team worked on a crisis intervention model, staying with the user until the situation was resolved and employing a problem-solving approach with others involved. Emergency medication was prescribed if appropriate. The case manager retained coordinating responsibility although other team members were sometimes involved in working with the user. The care plan was reviewed not less than once every six months.

At 18 months follow-up, 83% of DLP users had been admitted to hospital (versus 100% in the control condition) although admissions lasted approximately one-fifth the duration of the control group (mean 14 vs. 72 days, $p < 0.01$) (Muijen, 1990). No significant differences were found between the two conditions on measures of psychopathology, social functioning and user satisfaction (although trends favoured the DLP). A significant difference in favour of the DLP was found for the satisfaction of relatives of people presenting for their first admission (Muijen *et al.*, in press).

Comment

Four services demonstrating viable alternatives to hospital-based care have been described. Although none claims to be able to eliminate the need for asylum-based care completely, results suggest that assertive case management makes less use of in-patient beds, achieves increased user satisfaction and produces positive outcomes for service users without increased costs. These findings should not be surprising. Kiesler (1982) reviewed ten studies offering random assignment to in-patient care and a non-institutional alternative and found that none indicated better outcomes following hospitalization. On the contrary, the alternatives tended to produce better personal and social outcomes for users at no extra cost. He concludes, 'It seems quite clear . . . that for the vast majority of patients now being assigned to in-patient units in mental institutions, care of at least equal impact could be otherwise provided' (p. 357). Moreover, he continues, 'There is clear evidence . . . that the best predictor of hospitalization is prior hospitalization. These data . . . suggest quite clearly that hospitalization of mental patients is self-perpetuating' (p. 358). More recent reviews draw similar, if more conservative conclusions (e.g. Olfson, 1990; Taube *et al.*, 1990). The finding that assertive community treatment reduces hospitalization for high service users has proved a robust one, although some studies have found a compensatory increase in other services. Users consistently prefer community-based approaches to hospital-based care even though not all studies have found this correlates with perceived increases in quality of life.

Why then, in view of these robust and powerful findings, has the research not been translated into practice? Mosher (1983) suggests that one answer lies with his psychiatric colleagues: 'Over the past several decades psychiatry has experienced a rapprochement with the rest of medicine. . . . The growth of psychiatric wards in general hospitals has been part of this process. To ask psychiatry to move many of its therapeutic endeavours out of hospitals would be regarded as a disruption of its new relation with the rest of medicine. Hence, data about the effectiveness of alternatives are not greeted with great enthusiasm by the profession' (p. 1580). This was reiterated by Turner (1988) who also predicted concerns among his consultant psychiatrist colleagues over greater local availability of 'front-line clinical management', increased personal communication between social workers and community-based health service staff, a shift of attention towards the role of the family doctor, the abandonment of routine out-patient clinics, and an end to their reliance on ward-based junior medical staff. The importance of the attitudes of senior medical staff should be borne in mind when considering the even bigger challenge of persuading the general public that people with severe and long-term mental health problems are entitled and able to live ordinary lives in their communities.

SERVICES FOR ADULTS LIVING IN THE COMMUNITY

Bridge Programme, Chicago, USA

The Bridge was established in 1978 as a replication of the Madison project in a more deprived inner-city context. It also differed in that:

1. attention was specifically focused on the most frequent consumers of in-patient care rather than everybody presenting for admission;
2. the network of other providers was more dense, complex and fraught with bureaucratic obstacles;
3. the project had no control over admissions or what happened to the user when they were in one of the many hospitals, and
4. the Bridge was comparatively poorly resourced, with larger case loads and no 24-hour staffing.

All user contact took place in the community with about three-quarters pre-planned and the remainder occurring as needed. The work was summarized as '. . . the venerable social work techniques of friendly visiting and assertive inter-agency co-ordination combined with *in vivo* or on-the-spot training in social, vocational, and independent living skills' (Witheridge and Dincin, 1985, p. 66). A typical visit could start at the user's home and proceed to a nearby restaurant for coffee and conversation. They concentrated on concrete tasks such as doing the laundry or appeasing an unhappy landlord. Only after these basic needs were satisfied did the team turn to less tangible needs such as relationship problems or vocational aspirations. This emphasis on taking services to users was seen as indispensable. Although it was labour-intensive, time-consuming and took workers into unsavoury and unsafe parts of the city, users were felt to need on-the-spot help to solve problems of daily living that might otherwise cause crises and rehospitalization. Users often felt unwelcome at agencies to which they were referred and without assertive help would disappear, only to emerge again in crisis. The service featured a commitment to assertive resource coordination, a single point of responsibility to ensure coherence and continuity, and a firm 'no-close' policy. That meant that users could participate in the programme regardless of their level of dependence or disturbance.

For a sample of service users, the mean number of admissions dropped from 3.3 admissions in the year prior to their involvement in the project to 1.9 subsequently. The average number of days hospitalized went from 87.1 to 36.6 (Witheridge *et al.*, 1982). The authors felt that more admissions could have been prevented but for:

1. over-reaction to concrete problems that could be resolved more efficiently in context with less disruption;
2. the continued existence of incentives at organizational level for hospitals to maintain admissions whether they are strictly necessary or not;
3. inadequate cooperation between the hospital and community-based agencies (e.g. by hospital staff failing to consult involved community workers at admission, discharge or during the user's in-patient stay); and
4. the continued uncritical use of hospitals as a means to control behaviour construed as deviant.

One feature of the programme was a shared case load system whereby each worker saw every user on a rotating basis. This had the advantage of allowing the efficient deployment of workers during a crisis and allowed workers regular respite from users who were particularly difficult to work with. Also, users were less likely to be disturbed by the absence of any one worker due to illness or leave. The disadvantages were that a constant flow of information was demanded between workers which in turn demanded openness, good communication skills and stamina on the part of staff. The team met twice a day and there was much redundancy of communication.

The possibly deleterious effects of the absence of a committed relationship with one worker or important information being lost were not considered, although a later study examined the issue when comparing a CMHC with two CMHCs employing Bridge-trained workers (Bond *et al.*, 1988). All three CMHCs practised assertive case management and operated in large cities. In each site, users were randomly allocated to assertive case management or a control offering office-based case management. Eligible users had been discharged from hospital within the past year and either rehospitalized at least three times in the past two years or judged to be at risk of re-admission. Assertive case management resulted in reduced rehospitalization in the Bridge-trained teams (34% vs. 72%, and 9% vs. 48% rehospitalization; 7.7 days vs. 46.3 days, and no days vs. 20.3 days mean duration of stay). However, for the third team controls fared better and although assertive case management was cheaper it was not found to be cost-effective. The unsuccessful team had case managers operating in pairs rather than as a team and each worker was assigned an individual case load. This meant that users got less personal contact. The authors observed that as individual case load increased case managers acted more impersonally towards users. However, this team also differed in that it had a more insight-orientated and less pragmatic approach to clinical work which endorsed the idea of therapeutic hospitalization and emphasized the need for users to 'accept their illness'.

The success of psychosocial interventions in this study were primarily attributed to medication compliance. For example, pill counters were provided where users had difficulty reading or following instructions and case managers were assertive in refilling prescriptions. One Bridge-trained team reported improved communication around casework as an advantage of being part of a CMHC although there was also a risk of being drawn into other CMHC activities. Frequent meetings were considered central to preserving the sanity of staff.

Texas, USA

Franklin *et al.* (1987) randomly allocated 417 people with a recent history of hospital admission to case management or the usual CMHC provision. The case management service comprised one supervisor and seven case managers with an average of 4.3 years' experience working in mental health. Case managers spent 51% of their time delivering services to users, 39% acting as brokers for other services, and 10% on other activities such as travel, public relations, administration and training.

The study monitored re-admissions, use of other resources

and quality of life on a range of measures including objective social indicators, self-reports of satisfaction and assessments of activities of daily living, affect and self-esteem. Measures were taken before allocation and after one year. No differences were found on demographic or clinical profiles before allocation. However, after 12 months, 62 case-managed and 38 control subjects had been admitted to state or county hospitals (data from 38% of the sample were unobtainable at follow-up). Case-managed users stayed in hospital for longer periods and used community services a ratio of 2.35 times more frequently than the control subjects. No differences were found on use of medication. The case-managed group had an increased monthly income and improvements in employment status but no other improvements in quality of life were found. Increased use of services was not therefore seen to impact significantly on quality of life. The authors suggest this was due to the existing high levels of service provision supplied by other local providers.

Midwestern USA

Modrcin, Rapp and Poertner (1988) compared assertive with office-bound case management. The primary approaches to service delivery in the control group were attendance at a CMHC, counselling to alleviate immediate distress, and arrangement of services by phone. A collaborative relationship with users, community resource development or advocacy was not seen as crucial. In contrast, assertive case management emphasized user strengths along with needs, a collaborative approach via a personal relationship with the user, and assertive outreach. The assertive case managers were four half-time workers who had received five days' training but had no previous experience of paid work in human services. The six controls were Bachelor or Masters-level workers with an average of three years' experience.

Eighty-nine people referred over four months to a large midwestern CMHC were randomly assigned to each condition. Most were non-white and single, the average age was 26, and 61% were diagnosed with schizophrenia. The monitoring of practice revealed that the assertive case managers engaged in more contacts with the user, worked out of the office more, used more goal- rather than problem-orientated words and focused on strengths rather than diagnosis or pathology.

At follow-up, carers rated people who had received assertive case management as better adjusted in terms of community living skills and appropriate community behaviours. They were more likely than controls to be involved in vocational training, show an increase in tolerance of stress, and engage in more apparently meaningful leisure time activities. However, they did not do so well on socialization skills (the user's ability to be involved with people in a variety of settings), and this was the most powerful discriminator of the two groups. The authors suggested that this may have been because the assertive case managers rated users lower on this scale because they had greater expectations of their socialization skills.

Although assertive case management was superior over-all, given high case loads, a triage approach was suggested whereby assertive case management is used at the beginning of user contact, leading into the more usual case management practice after the user is stabilized and their coping skills for independent living adequately developed.

Spokane County, Washington, USA

Borland, McRae and Lycan (1989) compared the outcome of five years of intensive case management with the two year period prior to its introduction. They focused on young, difficult-to-serve, thought-disordered users with recent histories of admission. Eight case managers managed a case load of around nine users each.

A central feature of the service was the control of users' money to provide an incentive to attend for medication and other appointments, to prevent substance abuse, and pay for accommodation. This was a source of conflict between users and case managers. A 'work incentive fund' was also established to motivate users to do light domestic tasks or engage in voluntary work. The project had access to two crisis beds and two shelter rooms in a single-room occupancy hotel.

Readmissions reduced by 74%, and days spent in hospital

by 75%. Thirty per cent of users were not hospitalized at all. This group tended to be using structured residential care and engaging in less substance abuse. Crisis calls and assessments for involuntary admission fell dramatically over the period of the study. The decrease in hospital use coincided with increased use of the crisis beds and an increase in structured residential care of 193%. A follow-up study of people who had been transferred back to mainstream CMHC services found that the gains from five years of case management were largely maintained. The authors concluded that many users 'mature and stabilize', allowing them to cope with less intensive support (McRae *et al.*, 1990).

Kansas, USA

Rapp and Wintersteen (1989) reported 12 replications of their approach to case management over six years. Eighty-eight per cent of users were diagnosed with a major mental disorder, 92% had at least one hospitalization, and 72% had many. Often case managers were asked to work with people that the CMHC had given up on.

Only 15.5% of case-managed users returned to hospital, compared with 30% of people receiving the usual state services. One project fared badly (37% admission) and was characterized by fewer goals being set and a tendency to spend more time in the office than out in the community. Length of hospital stay was also reduced, apparently because the case managers remained involved and were ready to pick up the work following discharge. Projects attained 79% goal achievement with users and the number of goals set and their achievement increased over the six years. Advocacy work was found to take more time than anticipated. In comparing the case managers with mainstream agencies, it was noted that the former tended to set higher expectations and focus on ordinary community services (such as adult education) rather than segregating services. However, generalizations from this study are limited in that the case managers were Masters or Bachelor-level trainee social workers working with case loads of between two and seven for four months under the supervision of experienced social workers. Nonetheless, the impact of case management training within this context seems to be considerable.

Mississippi, USA

Most studies prescribe the tasks of case management and then evaluate the outcome. In contrast, Fisher *et al*. (1988) described the practice of existing case management services in 15 CMHCs and one state hospital to determine which tasks influence outcome. Of 1214 users, 62% were black, 50% had between one and three previous admissions, 9% were waged, around 60% were diagnosed with schizophrenia, and 95% were on psychotropic medication.

Case managers were paraprofessionals supervized by workers with Masters degrees or ten years' experience as case managers. Training was limited to self-study materials and supervision. The case management role included assessment, objective setting and planning, referral and linkage to other services, advocacy, monitoring and transportation. The authors predicted that advocacy and referral would have the greatest positive impact as these were the distinguishing features of case management. This was not borne out. In fact, monitoring was the best predictor of global change, problem number and severity. Transportation predicted global change and problem number.

They attributed this negative finding to:

1. the emphasis on crisis intervention and lack of time to offer advocacy or linkage to other services;
2. user relapse as the stimulus for increased service input;
3. a rural location which increased the relative importance of transportation services, and
4. the paucity of services to link to.

On this latter point they compare their findings to the Texas service described above which concluded that a high level of local service provision also reduces the impact of case management on quality of life measures.

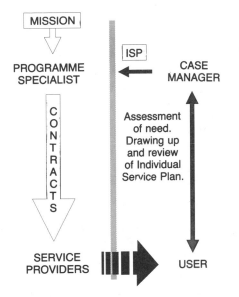

Figure 3.1 The Massachusetts approach to case management.

Holyoke/Chicopee, Western Massachusetts, USA

This service arose from the closure of a large institution and exemplifies the role of case management within a needs-led service system (Smith, 1990b). The case management service comprised a director, two clinical supervisors and 11 case managers. Referrals were via the Director of Case Management from any source including family or self-referral. Eligibility was based upon past hospitalization, and risk of hospitalization or homelessness. Each case manager was assigned a case load of around 34. Figure 3.1 shows the context of case management within the wider service system.

The case manager had the task of assessing individual need and drawing up an individual service plan (ISP). This statement of the user's needs was then presented to a programme specialist who was responsible for fulfilling the demands identified through contracted service provision. The state-funded purchasing agency contracted with around 14 different corporations through a variety of contracts. Contracts were only made with not-for-profit agencies since the profit motive was not seen to promote good practice. Values-based training was a precondition for the award of contracts. This led to a shared understanding of the problems facing people with mental health problems, and agreement over appropriate forms of intervention. Shared training also led to less inter-disciplinary conflict.

Service providers had to accept someone if the programme specialist referred them to an empty slot. The result of this service provision was then monitored by the case manager. Eligibility for allocation to a contracted programme was based upon a very clear mission statement concerning who is defined as most in need. In this way, if an ISP was not fulfilled, at least it could be stated with confidence that people in greater need were being served. All independent sector and state employees had three days of training in the service mission.

The separation of the case manager-user relationship from the system that purchases and contracts for service provision was crucial. Case managers did not hold budgets and were not involved in resource disputes. Since the case managers had the job of assessing need without simultaneously weighing up the resources available, the ISPs were an uncontaminated resource of information on unmet need. This information guided the commissioning and contracting of service provision through a 'purchase of service' cycle involving:

1. planning based on an assessment of needs among the target client group achieved through an aggregation of ISPs;
2. the subsequent issuing by the commissioning office of 'requests for proposals' which invited agencies to bid for contracts to provide the required services;
3. contract development concentrating on measurable outcomes for users;
4. monitoring, which included site visits by programme specialists from the purchasing agency; and
5. evaluation, including an annual summary. Since the summary informed the needs assessment and thus the requests for proposals, the whole process was cyclical.

The commissioning office balanced the level of competition among providers. Too little inhibited good practice and reduced choice, while too much threatened stability within the provider system, programmes came and went and users experienced severe discontinuity. Each programme was encouraged to become a specialist in a particular field, thereby encouraging comprehensive provision and discouraging territorial disputes.

Rockland County, USA

This service was initially designed to serve a de-institutionalized elderly population. However, over time, increasing numbers of young adults with long-term and severe mental health problems were referred. They tended to be geographically mobile, resisting treatment from any one programme but making heavy demands on emergency and in-patient services. Around 70% were diagnosed with schizophrenia, and 11% with personality disorder. Approximately 85% to 90% engaged in substance abuse.

Case managers concentrated on motivating users and coordinating services. Their role was to 'initiate an individualized and coordinated service plan based on careful assessment for each user, including users who are not currently engaged in treatment' (Berzon and Lowenstein, 1984, p. 50). The service grew rapidly to three teams of eight or nine case managers with case loads of 35 to 45 users. About a fifth of the users were felt to make particularly heavy demands on the time and emotional resources of case managers, requiring 'the highest level of clinical, coordinating and intervention skills, along with almost superhuman tolerance for frustration and ambiguity' (p. 50).

Within the state, case management had a positive effect in reducing the number of hospitalizations and where admission was unavoidable, the duration was shorter. Factors considered important to these successful outcomes included:

1. variety and flexibility of roles in order to deal with the whole person and their difficulties;
2. thorough assessment of users' needs and strengths in order to set achievable goals;
3. matching users to case managers according to the latter's skills and personality style. Case managers also specialized

(e.g. family therapy, work with people from ethnic minorities, substance abusers, and users involved in the criminal justice system);

4. individualized service planning;
5. the maintenance of a relationship between case manager and user regardless of all factors except the user's needs. This included close liaison with in-patient facilities. Case managers attended hospital discharge screening meetings;
6. limited case loads;
7. a team approach to provide a structure for support and supervision. Trusted help was available in a crisis and workers could substitute for each other if a case manager was unavailable for any reason. It also allowed accessible back-up from supervisors, the prevention of burn-out though regular supervision, ongoing training, peer support, realistic goal setting, and the development of a culture that emphasized accepting the limits of one's own and the user's resources;
8. high levels of inter-agency communication to facilitate rapid and effective responses from service providers, resolve conflict, and prevent duplication and gaps in services. Case conferences were the main forum for this communication. Securing welfare benefits for users was found to be a particularly crucial but specialized and time-consuming activity.
9. the autonomy of the service. This was felt to promote freedom in planning, decision-making, advocacy and coordination, thereby allowing a continuous but flexible service.

SERVICES FOR PEOPLE DISCHARGED FROM HOSPITAL

Toronto, Canada

Most case management services are community-based and follow the user into hospital. Goering *et al.* (1988) examined the outcome of a case management service introduced after hospital admission. The service had eight workers, four of which had professional training. All had intensive training in community service coordination skills which emphasized linking users to resources and user-centred interviewing. User involvement and the development of personal relationships between user and case manager were central to practice. Case managers performed assessments, developed rehabilitation plans, linked users with community resources, monitored progress and advocated on behalf of users. This sometimes included activities aimed at developing resources. Case managers were out-posted to four in-patient units and carried case loads of between 15 and 20.

Criteria for admission to the service were long-term mental health problems, poor employment history, social isolation and residential instability. The study evaluated outcome at two years using matched controls. The sample was drawn at random and users were matched for sex, hospital location, number of previous admissions, diagnosis and employment status. The groups did not differ significantly on any other demographic or clinical characteristic. At admission to the units, 77% were diagnosed psychotic, 60% were single, 53% had more than five previous admissions, and 44% were involuntary admissions. Interviews were carried out by research workers.

The case-managed group reported higher occupational functioning, more independent living, and less social isolation at two years. However, no differences were found in number of admissions or length of stay. The authors attribute the lack of impact on hospitalization to an emphasis on improving functioning rather than intervening in crisis to prevent admission, the unavailability of alternative approaches to episodes of severe disturbance, and the limited role of case managers in controlling medical and other kinds of therapy.

The two areas that caused users most distress and difficulty, social isolation and occupational functioning, were also the areas in which case management achieved most impact. Improvements paralleled increased use of services. The case-managed users made more use of vocational, educational, housing, social, recreational and financial services.

The authors stressed the importance of committed personal relationships between users and case managers, and the need for small case loads. Users were reported to value the support that case managers offered and the fact that they were able to step into the breach where services were unavailable.

The PSSRU Care in the Community projects, UK

In 1983, the British Government funded a wave of demonstration projects for people leaving long-stay hospital care (Renshaw *et al.*, 1988; Knapp *et al.*, 1992). Case management was a precondition of funding for all 28 projects and there was a wide range of contrasting models of practice and service configurations. Eight projects served people with mental health problems.

An incremental approach to service development emerged. For example, criteria for entry into the services developed with experience and changes in circumstance. Operational delays meant that criteria became obsolete, potential users became anxious and occasionally disagreements between projects and other agencies flared up. Formal assessment instruments used to determine the projects' client groups were generally not found to contribute to successful planning. Some projects made use of alternative forms of assessment such as observation or 'getting-to-know-you' programmes (Brost and Johnson, 1982). Almost all projects made use of individual care plans. Most used tailor-made approaches to fit in with the particular philosophy of the service and the needs of users. Some (e.g. the Islington project) were able to take a developmental approach, adapting their planning and record systems in the light of experience. Projects varied over whether the responsibility for preparing individual service plans lay with case managers or the team as a whole. Almost all involved users in reviews although there was considerable variation in how this took place. Most projects reviewed cases over intervals of six months or less and many augmented these reviews with more frequent informal ones.

Projects ranged from those that placed all the case management responsibility with one person, such as an officer in charge of a home, to those where responsibility was devolved to team members, often in the form of a keyworker role (Cambridge, 1992). In the majority, case managers were responsible for coordinating service inputs from mainstream health and social services, and across a wider mixed economy of provision. In only two projects (Maidstone and Darlington) did case managers hold a budget for individual users although ring-fenced budgets for groups of users were more common. One mental health project (Brent) felt that budget-holding would compromise the case manager's advocacy role. On resource management, Cambridge (1992) underlined the need for working cost information right from the start of the project in order to achieve the fair and equitable distribution of resources across a group of people with diverse and changing needs.

Projects were also divided according to whether they offered mobile service delivery (16 projects), or whether the work was facility-based (12 projects). The scale and geographical context of the projects proved to be important predictors of organization, with larger projects tending to favour multidisciplinary teams, involvement of other agencies in the individual care planning, the delegation of responsibility to keyworkers, and mobile service delivery (Cambridge, 1992).

SERVICES FOR HOMELESS PEOPLE

Project HELP Manhattan, USA

Between 1955 and 1984, the numbers in New York State mental hospitals plummeted from 90 000 to 21 000, with inadequate re-provision in the community. Project HELP (Homeless Emergency Liaison Project) was developed 'in response to the need for rapid transport of [homeless, at-risk people with mental health problems] to a hospital when a life-threatening emergency was encountered' (Putnam, Cohen and Sullivan, 1986, p. 113). It covered most of Manhattan and was staffed by psychiatrists, nurses and social workers. The project was unique in that the psychiatrists were given the authority to transport anyone who was 'imminently at risk to self or others' (*ibid.*, p. 113) to an emergency room for assessment. Around 50% of referrals were by phone, from police, mental health and social service professionals, and members of the public. When not responding to phone calls, project staff patrolled the streets in a radio-equipped van. Usually one worker approached someone who appeared to be distressed or disturbed while other staff stood near by.

They described the service as being for people 'camping out' and there was no mention of doctors or hospitals. Even so, they noted that the individual may 'flee when anyone attempts to approach them. If they do not flee they may crawl more deeply into their cardboard boxes or try to conceal themselves completely under the blankets' (*ibid.*, p. 116). They found around 40% of users refused to cooperate and were therefore assessed by observation only, 40% consented to a partial interview and 20% to a full interview. Repeated contact often failed to engage users and assessments used information gleaned from local shopkeepers or residents. Services offered included food, clothing, legal assistance, delousing, showers and shaves, detoxification, and referral and transportation to an emergency room or to a clinic or shelter.

The frequency of repeated efforts at assessment and engagement depended on assessed risk. The team employed four categories of risk, with users moving between them, usually in the direction of greater risk. They were:

1. 'imminent risk' people who did not need police input but were nonetheless transported involuntarily to the emergency room (around 3% of the project's population);
2. 'high risk and maladaptive' people who were seriously impaired but not a danger to themselves or others. They were closely monitored and involuntarily transported if they deteriorated (around 35%);
3. 'high risk but adaptive' people who were overtly crazy but had adapted to street life. They were regularly monitored (around 55%);
4. 'minimal risk' people who were homeless, episodic users of services (around 7%).

High risk users were seen as often as possible. Of 1309 persons evaluated over 30 months, 61 were involuntarily transported to emergency rooms. There were 271 voluntary admissions.

Project HELP employed aspects of assertive case management. It provided food and clothing and established links for accessing shelter care. It also provided medical and psychiatric services on the street if necessary. However, there are significant omissions. There is little emphasis on individual workers or the team as a whole acting as a continuous contact point for users, nor does the team take responsibility for longer term outcome. Such projects can be viewed as coercive approaches to clearing the streets of undesirable and unwanted people with scant regard for their longer term benefit. Indeed, Project HELP has prompted an outcry from those concerned with the abuse of civil rights associated with its special powers to take people off the streets. This 'sweep mentality' pervades many services concerned with homeless people (Onyett, 1991a) and should be resisted if assertive outreach is to be anything more than a cosmetic exercise. Less coercive alternatives are available: for example, Project Reach Out, a team that operates in and around Central Park in New York, attempts to involve users in their programmes over very long periods by approaching them with an 'engagement tool'; a brown paper bag containing fruit juice, a sandwich and some information. The workers manage to combine assertive outreach with a respectful and considerate regard for people without homes that acknowledges their right to remain at liberty.

The Skid Row Mental Health Service, Los Angeles, USA

This service was founded on an acknowledgement that people living on 'Skid Row' are 'highly independent individuals who would suffer starvation, homelessness and dehumanization rather than lose their freedom' (Hospital and Community Psychiatry, 1986). The project started in a situation where relationships between social service staff and users were very poor. Interviews were being conducted through a half-inch thick glass partition with wire mesh and users were asked to hand over weapons before passing through a metal detector. Case management, medication management and crisis intervention were the primary forms of intervention. Case managers were psychiatric nurses, psychologists, psychiatric social workers, and paraprofessional community workers. They offered crisis intervention, assessment and referral for the most difficult-to-serve users and worked jointly with social services staff to whom they also provided education and consultation.

It soon became clear that mental health services for homeless people had to be on 'their turf'. Linking to agencies outside the area was a failure. Only when the project began to 'piggy back' mental health services onto existing services for homeless people were they able to reach people with severe mental health problems. This meant gaining the trust of mission volunteers, many of whom were 'graduates of the streets'.

A drop-in was offered where people could get a psychiatric assessment without an appointment. As with Project Reach Out, psychiatrists became involved on a voluntary basis. Staff were always on duty to do screening assessments and refer to other services. If a user required hospitalization staff were empowered to take a 72-hour hold on them.

A range of programmes provided assistance in obtaining disability benefits, low cost transportation passes, medical care and other benefits, and staff psychiatrists performed the psychiatric assessments necessary to establish eligibility. Legal advocacy was available and an employee of the social security administration helped applicants fill out application forms. With the user's permission, the social security administration sent their mail to the clinic post office box, allowing staff to keep abreast of the application and alert the user to any need to take further action to obtain benefits.

A socialization programme employed three recreational therapists to work with people who were not able to cope with a more structured programme. They went on 'outings', watched television or engaged in arts and crafts. Disability cheques were sent to project staff so that they could pay the user's rent and bills and then help them decide how to spend the rest of the money. Project staff reported that as users attended for money, they became involved in the other programmes offered. Around 85% of users in the money management programme used other services. Group work was very open and informal. People did not have to make a commitment to attend and a 'loose therapeutic relationship and limited goal setting' was employed.

Some people arrived in Los Angeles as a result of 'Greyhound therapy', the practice of giving crazy people a one-way ticket out of town. Outreach work included intercepting these people at the bus terminal. Anyone who appeared to be in need of help was escorted to the drop-in and staff attempted to contact families to establish whether the person could go home.

The project joined with other agencies to form Concerned Agencies of Metropolitan Los Angeles, a private non-profit corporation. This improved relationships between agencies, particularly the police. With their greater understanding of mental distress the police were more likely to take people to the drop-in rather than have them hospitalized.

The principle of piggy-backing mental health services on other services for homeless people has also been applied in Britain. Although results were only available for one year, an evaluation of a service attached to hostels for single homeless men recommended assertive case management offered by a clearly managed multidisciplinary team (Psychiatric Team for Single Homeless People, 1990).

Drug and alcohol abuse are between three and six times more prevalent among homeless people when compared with the general population (Mulkern and Spense, 1984). However, mental health providers commonly refuse to work with people who are diagnosed as substance abusers, and substance abuse services frequently exclude people with severe and long-term mental health problems because of difficult-to-manage behaviour or because their use of psychotropic medication is seen as substituting one addiction for another. As a result, people with severe and long-term mental health problems and an addiction often receive no service instead of both services (Fariello and Scheidt, 1989). Through providing an accessible and comprehensive approach to assessment and provision, case management may go some way to resolving this split.

SERVICES FOR OTHER CLIENT GROUPS

Three approaches are described below that highlight issues concerning the practice of case management in general.

Thanet Community Care Project, Thanet, England

The first detailed account of case management published in Britain focused on providing an alternative to residential care for frail older people (Challis and Davies, 1986). Case managers were specially trained social workers committed to coordinating a network of services to users, and were an integral part of the local social services department. The case management role included identifying users in need, working with them to develop a comprehensive service plan based on their needs and goals, and helping them to obtain appropriate services, support and entitlements.

A central feature of this system was decentralized budgets. Case managers were able to spend a budget equivalent to two-thirds of the cost of providing residential care. The money was calculated per user, per week and could be spent on 'services or developments needed to maintain elderly people in the community and improve their quality of life' (*ibid.*, p. 9). Expenditure beyond this amount required line management approval and so acted as a trigger for management consultation.

Operation of the system required a number of other important features. These were a problem-orientated recording system for resource monitoring, clearly defined case loads, and the strict costing of service packages. This allowed feedback to case managers on their work through a system of peer review. Case managers were able to consider the distribution of resources within their case load in order to test whether there was any bias against particular users or carers.

Case management achieved positive outcomes on quality of life and quality of care measures, when compared with a control group. Fewer users went into residential care, and fewer died. The service was found to be cost-effective, particularly for very dependent older people receiving considerable informal support, and relatively isolated people who were moderately dependent but suffering from long-term non-psychotic mental health problems. However, the client group was quite a select one. Although people needed to display 'inadequate social functioning sufficient to consider a move away from independent living' (*ibid.*, p. 27) they were excluded from the evaluation if they were admitted to institutional care between referral and two weeks after the assessment, or if 'aspects of the client's physical or mental condition led to a decision by the team not to provide support'. Examples of the latter included 'stubborn independence', being 'inaccessible through extreme deafness', dementia, unwillingness to accept help, or long-term depression and anxiety. Of 202 potential cases for the experimental group, 92 actually entered the study.

Managing a budget proved highly advantageous. It paid for items such as heating appliances and automatic kettles as well as more unusual assets such as assistance from local people. The helpers and users were very carefully matched with consideration of attitude and personality, the helpers' past experience, and their capacity to deal with unpleasant experiences and uncertainty. Sometimes the helper was already known to the user. Support for helpers was provided through a network of coffee mornings and the back-up of case managers. The devolved budgeting system also clearly identified the limits of autonomy and accountability and allowed for meaningful collection of information on resource allocation. It is important to stress that very little resource rationing was involved as only five cases exceeded their budget limit. As a result the authors claim no practical or ethical issues were encountered. This is an important consideration in view of the tremendous influence that the Thanet project has had on the development of case management in Britain.

CHOICE – The Case Management Service, London, England

This service for people with physical handicaps was unusual in that central to its philosophy was the need for case managers to be independent of service providers in order to allow their whole-hearted allegiance to users. Its funding was independent of any service purchasing or providing agency.

Case managers coordinated a comprehensive assessment, agreed goals with the user, drew up a plan of action, co-ordinated service inputs, monitored the progress of the plan's implementation, checked at a later stage to allow for any changes in circumstances, and recorded and reported any short-falls in service provision to planners and managers. The case manager carried an advocate role and represented the user if requested. A primary therapist role was not assumed, and if the user needed counselling a referral to a social worker was made. For most of the duration of the project the service had only one full-time and one part-time case manager, and an administrator.

A thorough evaluation of the project was carried out incorporating the views of users and other service providers (Pilling,

1988). From May 1986 to September 1987, 142 users were seen although this was felt to be an underestimate of the demand. This was indicated by occupational therapists who felt that the project only managed to obtain priority for their users at the expense of other, less articulate users. This underlines the need for target efficiency, particularly where resources are scarce. The project performed no outreach work and relied on referrals.

Around three-quarters of the project's users expressed satisfaction with the service. However, this did not differ significantly from a comparison group of people who had seen social workers and occupational therapists. Nonetheless, the project was heavily used by users and service providers, suggesting that a significant gap in service provision was being filled.

The issue of resource allocation was a central concern of users. When asked what could have been more satisfactory about the service, the most frequent response (27%) was a call for case managers to have more 'power or resources'. On the other hand, service providers felt that the independence of the service was crucial to their user-centred approach and emphasis on advocacy. They felt case managers had greater influence over services than workers managed by health or social services. This is partly because project workers were perceived as being more free to make contacts and cross boundaries in a way that could cause territorial disputes among statutory workers. However, some service providers felt that, given adequate time and resources, they themselves could take on case management tasks such as developing a knowledge base of alternatives for service provision and linking users to them. Overall Pilling concluded that case management services needed to retain an identity separate from mainstream services while not appearing to be antagonistic to them. One suggested solution was that the service becomes a separate unit within social services with managerial responsibility over other departments.

Brokerage models

Although not defined as case management, service brokerage is worthy of mention because of its parallels with independent models of case management such as CHOICE, and the importance afforded to devolved budgets in British case management. To date, they have mainly focused on people with learning difficulties or physical disabilities.

Service brokerage identifies the central problem of service provision as the lack of decision-making responsibility and power placed with users. Providers are financed directly, bypassing the person needing the service. The aim of service brokerage is that devolved individualized funding should allow users to choose from a marketplace of provision, and exert direct control over expenditure concerning their lives. Individualized funding also means that service provision can be more flexible and easily monitored. Increased community integration is sought through less emphasis on special provision and blocks of care, and the avoidance of initiating a ghetto for people with similar problems by lumping them together in the same place.

At the Community Living Society, Vancouver, brokers were managed by a brokerage board which was controlled and led by users and carers. Their job was to help users identify their needs and the services to meet them. They acted for users and did not enter into any contracts with service providers or funding authorities without instruction from them. Their role was described as similar to that of a social worker only without the conflict of interest inherent in being an employee of an authority with limited resources. Subsequently, service brokerage evolved into a number of different models relying on a strong computerized information resource, peer support through volunteer commitment, and natural support networks.

Brokerage is promoted as a form of service provision that is conceptually distinct from case management (Brandon and Towe, 1989) although it is unclear how it differs in practice. Individualized funding and the independence of the employing organization from providers may both be incorporated into case management and have the potential to confer both costs and benefits. Placing resource management responsibility with brokers may not in itself place power in the hands of the user. Brokers should be subject to the same safeguards on practice as case managers. Indeed, Brandon and Towe (1989) discuss the need for codes of practice for brokers, and a range of brokerage services in order to promote choice (leading to the intriguing idea of broker brokers).

Successful brokerage relies on working alongside personal networks of committed individuals who form a group, with four principles guiding their work with individuals: promotion of choice, an individual focus, emphasis on efforts towards environmental change, and integration with the local community. Their role is to meet needs for friendship and caring, focus on the uniqueness of the individual, support his or her decision-making, monitor the work of service providers, and provide checks and balances for people making decisions on behalf of individuals who are not able to make those decisions themselves. This latter task is critical. Brandon and Towe (1989) describe how, when users cannot give meaningful consent, the personal network 'has to create reasonable assumptions out of its knowledge of the handicapped person, with all the dangers of that process' (p. 32).

Service brokerage leaves a number of important questions unanswered. How does brokerage accommodate people who really cannot manage their own affairs and also have difficulty creating or maintaining networks? Does having an existing network influence your access to brokerage? Does a total reliance on individualized funding mean there is a risk that users are isolated from others who might, if they were able to come together, constitute a more powerful lobby? A core principle of service brokerage is the acceptance of any user, regardless of disability or diagnosis, in order to avoid users being endlessly passed from one agency to another. What is it about being an independent agency that means the service can take all comers seeking assistance? The need to prioritize resources and target particular client groups appears to be side-stepped.

Despite these reservations, service brokerage does serve to underline issues of good practice, such as having committed independent advocates working alongside resource coordinators and, most importantly, the need to place choice with users.

CONCLUSIONS

Despite the methodological problems described at the beginning of the chapter, ten tentative conclusions can be drawn:

1. Case management services must be very clear about who they are aiming to serve.
2. Assertive case management may be particularly useful for people who have most difficulty making use of services (e.g. homeless people) although there is a risk that services can become overly controlling.
3. Assertive case management produces better outcomes than office-bound case management.
4. Assertive case management reduces the use of hospital beds for people at risk of admission.
5. Assertive case management can achieve good outcomes for users and carers without increased cost.
6. The effectiveness of the case manager's role as a resource coordinator is highly dependent on the context. In very well-resourced localities case management may be redundant, and in impoverished areas case managers may find they have no services to coordinate.
7. Personal relationships between users and case managers, individualized service planning and continuous support are important features of case management.
8. The use of medication, the devotion of considerable time and energy to advocacy work (e.g. regarding welfare entitlements) and attention to practical problems of everyday living may also be key features.
9. The relative importance of the different tasks of case management depends upon the needs of the client group and the demands of the environment (e.g. large rural catchment areas may place greater emphasis on transportation services).
10. In some contexts it may be important for case managers to be independent of service providers in order to be able to provide advocacy and unbiased monitoring. In others, case managers must be able to step into the breach as a provider when no other alternatives are available.

As stated at the beginning of this chapter, seekers after absolute psychological truth in service evaluation would do better to adopt a more pragmatic approach. The people with the responsibility for developing case management services need to be very clear about the information they need in order to evaluate options for service design. Since it is impossible to be prescriptive, the question remains, 'What particular form of case management will best meet the needs of this particular client group in this particular location?'. The next chapter examines some of the options.

Chapter 4

Organizational issues

Before considering the day-to-day practice of case management it is necessary to consider some of the broader organizational issues. This chapter examines some of the key questions to be asked when establishing a case management system.

WHICH CLIENT GROUP?

Most case management projects in Britain have been aimed at users with continuing needs, such as frail older people, people with learning difficulties and people experiencing the effects of long-term institutionalization. The continuity of contact offered by case managers is particularly appropriate to the long-term nature of their problems. So how should people with long-term mental health problems be prioritized for case management services?

Traditionally, psychiatric services have differentiated between acute services and long-stay provision for 'chronic' cases, each with their own resources and management structures. British case management has concentrated most attention on 'long-stay' users as they leave hospital. However, as stated by the House of Commons Social Services Committee (1985), 'The vast majority of mentally ill and mentally handicapped people are not and may never be in hospital. The almost obsessive concentration in public policy on the mechanisms for "getting people out of hospital" has sometimes obscured the basic fact that most mentally ill or mentally handicapped people already live in the community. If the presently uneven balance of concern is not redressed, all energies will be bent on providing services for people coming out of hospital, only to find equal pressure to use those facilities coming from people not currently in hospital.' The pressure is already there. The 'old long-stay' users are already being replaced by younger 'new long-term': people who may not have spent protracted periods in hospital, yet have repeated and long-term contact with services. Pepper and Ryglewicz (1984) summarize the situation in the US thus: 'Only within this generation has the young adult chronic patient population emerged as a full-blown community phenomenon, a real life illustration of how severe chronic mental disorders interact in the crucible of the community with the stresses and hazards of social life and with the distinguishing circumstances of youth. We have had to come to know the uninstitutionalized young adult patient, just as in a previous era we had to come to know the person shaped by the institutional environment . . .' (pp. 111–13). High re-admission rates suggest that the 'acute' versus 'chronic' distinction misses the point. People presenting with severe but apparently short-term problems clearly require greater support if re-admissions to hospital are to be prevented.

In addition to the 'new long-term' there are the 'new long-stay': a group of people being added to the old long-stay population, often for social rather than clinical reasons (Shepherd, 1984). However, this categorizing of people according to the way they use services may obscure individual and unique patterns of need, and promote gross planning methodologies. It would certainly be naive to assert that people are engaged in mental health services purely according to their needs. Available resources and social inequalities (e.g. due to race) also play a part (Chapter 1). Although past contact with mental health services, including long-term institutional care, may be an indicator of vulnerability, it should not be allowed to obscure other more current social and environmental factors.

Diagnosis and clinical factors are also often used to differentiate groups of users for the purposes of service provision. However, social factors are far superior in predicting the onset, course and outcome of mental distress and the ways people make use of services (Huxley, 1990). Clearly, there is a need for services to be more sophisticated about how they identify long-term need.

Given the heterogeneity of problems that people bring to mental health services, it follows that greater emphasis should be placed on the needs that people present *now*, taking account of factors such as the availability of other supports and security of accommodation, rather than provide a service purely on the basis of past residency in long-stay hospitals, age or diagnosis. Coordinated services aimed at promoting coping and reducing vulnerability to stress can then be put in place on the basis of a comprehensive and thorough assessment of current needs and strengths.

If case management services are responsive to changing needs they may be better able to operate a policy of minimal intervention in order to avoid creating dependency and undermining users' autonomy. In theory then, case management could be offered to a wide range of people with the expectation that support could be systematically withdrawn when support services are put in place. This would be achieved through regular reviews, and easy access back into the system should users require further help after their case is closed. However, in practice this assumption is not a sound one on which to base case management practice. Although the *patterns* of service use may change for most users, the *amount* of input needed may not be expected to decrease until the fourth or fifth year of case management, if at all (Harris and Bergman, 1988). It also assumes that adequate provision is available to ensure long-term support.

There is, then, a need to use rational criteria when deciding which people are to be given priority for assistance. The imperative to serve those most in need first is heightened by the possibility that, as resources for service provision decline, the threshold for access to assessment is likely to rise. Whatever criteria are used, it is crucial that their use is closely monitored in order to ensure that the service fulfils its objectives and those people not being served can be easily identified. The development of these criteria should also be informed by continuous needs assessment at locality level. Information is needed to counter the tendency for need to be defined according to the therapeutic inclinations, beliefs and assumptions of providers.

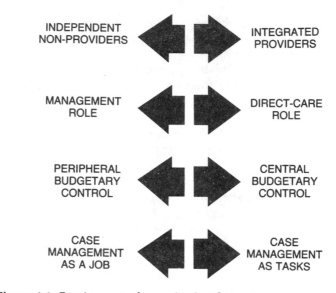

Figure 4.1 Continuums of organizational structure.

HOW INDEPENDENT OF PROVIDERS SHOULD CASE MANAGEMENT BE?

Figure 4.1 illustrates four heavily inter-related continuums of organization. They refer to the independence of case managers from provider agencies, the amount of time they spend in personal contact with users, their control over resources for individual service planning, and whether case management is best considered as a specialist job designation or a set of tasks that can be undertaken within other roles. Two radically different approaches to case management are represented at the extremes of these continuums. The Department of Health (1990) advocates the practices shown on the left-hand side of Figure 4.1, whereby case managers are independent from service providers, and are mainly concerned with coordinating and purchasing care. Case managers are specifically distinguished from 'keyworkers' whose role is to maintain contact with users. Keyworkers usually work for the main provider agency involved and will themselves have a major role in providing personal assistance.

The rationale for the case management/provider split is the need for case managers to avoid conflicts of interest. Case managers working for provider agencies may bias individual service planning in favour of their own agency and lack objectivity in monitoring. Users and carers may feel less able to voice complaints via the case manager if the case manager is part of the problem.

It has been assumed that independent case management agencies are in a more powerful position to act as advocates in the interests of users (e.g. CHOICE). In the model of case management advocated by the Department of Health, case managers will be purchaser-led and therefore only indepen- dent in a limited sense. As employees of purchasing agencies there is no guarantee that they will be concerned with main- taining high service quality or a vociferous advocacy role. Indeed, since they will be accountable to agencies with limited resources, the opposite may be predicted.

Independent case management services may be established to serve particular functions such as outreach work, assess- ment, or a single access point for users and referrers within a locality. This approach has significant advantages in terms of case-finding and gatekeeping. However, services that simply assess and refer on cannot be said to be practising case man- agement as the core tasks are separated. Assessment of people with long-term needs is an ongoing process involving the continuous monitoring of outcomes. It is not a one-shot screening and allocation process. Case managers need to maintain a coordinating and monitoring role.

Independent case managers may also encounter difficulties in liaising with providers in the mental health system who may find their authority difficult to accept. The providers may feel they should perform their own assessments to determine eligibility for the assistance they have on offer. Problems may arise if case managers prescribe certain forms of provision on the basis of their assessments that conflict with the perceived professional autonomy and decision-making powers of pro- viders. Professional providers may find themselves accountable to a case manager who they may perceive as having little expertise or understanding of their roles. This is likely to be particularly problematic where the case manager and provider have different professional backgrounds (e.g. if the case manager is a social worker and the provider is a doctor). Mueller and Hopp (1987) described similar inter-agency conflict surrounding a service where case managers had no legal or administrative power to enforce their recommendations. One resolution is to establish case management arrangements that do not extend beyond the case manager's own health or social services organization, and that therefore do not bridge the health and social care divide. However, clearly this sacrifices case management's potential for overcoming problems of fragmented and discontinuous care.

Independence from providers is represented as a continuum, as degrees of independence are possible. The continuum ranges from completely independent case managers employed by separate organizations dedicated purely to case management at one end, to mainstream service providers undertaking case management tasks at the other. Between these are services that may be within provider agencies but achieve degrees of independence through separate management structures or strong team identification. The resulting sense of autonomy may be an important predictor of service effectiveness (Berzon and Lowenstein, 1984).

The integration of any provider within a provider system is influenced by historical factors and territorial issues. Existing service providers may be wary of the effect of a new agency seeking integration because of concerns over the impact on their own established working patterns. This will be particularly so if the new provider agency assumes a high profile and stresses coordinating care for their users through a case management system. This was certainly the experience of the EIS during its early development and has also been reported elsewhere (e.g. Witheridge and Dincin, 1985). Although the effect of competition within a mixed economy of health and social care has yet to be fully experienced in Britain, it is unlikely that it will be a force for integration or cooperation between agencies. Mueller and Hopp (1987) observed that where agencies are reimbursed according to the number of users seen, there is effectively competition for customers and less inter-agency cooperation.

HOW MUCH DIRECT CONTACT SHOULD CASE MANAGERS HAVE WITH USERS?

The right-hand side of the continuums of Figure 4.1 approximates to the American approach to case management in mental health described in Chapter three. American case management is similar to the role of a travel *guide* escorting the user through a maze of service providers (Kanter, 1989), whereas the British approach is more akin to the role of a travel *agent* acting as broker for other services and directing people to them according to their needs. The American approach stresses direct contact with users over long periods. In many services the case manager role specifically includes the tasks of key-worker or primary therapist. In contrast, the British approach is exemplified by services where the case manager is placed further up the management hierarchy and has the job of coordinating or managing direct-care staff (e.g. the Thanet and Darlington Community Care Projects for older people). Since the case managers have a brokerage role they must remain dispassionate and uninvolved with users in order to ensure a balanced and fair approach to resource allocation.

The placing of the case manager in the managerial hierarchy depends upon which aspects of the role are to be emphasized. This in turn depends upon the needs of the client group. Mental health service providers are increasingly finding themselves working with users who are difficult to engage in services. They may, for example, be homeless and difficult to meet, or susceptible to crises. For many of these alienated and isolated individuals, identification is a priority and assessment may be problematic. Case managers therefore need to be direct-care staff who are mobile enough to bring their assessment skills into play in a variety of settings. This assertiveness in reaching out to users is a critical predictor of positive outcomes (Chapter 3). Users living in rural areas with few other services available may also have a greater need for contact with skilled direct-care staff. Indeed, it is difficult to identify any groups with severe and long-term mental health problems who would not need their case managers to be direct-care workers able to develop the quality of relationship with users needed to adequately assess their needs, make informed decisions and help guide them through complicated and bureaucratic service systems (Lamb, 1980). Presently these skills reside with people in provider roles.

Integrating case management with a direct-care provider role also helps reduce the risk of discontinuity where a primary therapist role is relevant to the user's needs. Lamb (1980) asks '... what is the rationale of the therapist going through an intermediary case manager to make the referral and provide all the information rather than making the referral himself?' (pp. 763–4). This adds another opportunity for breakdown of communication that is avoided if the therapy and case management tasks are located with the same worker. For some therapeutic issues it may be absolutely crucial that continuity is maintained with a highly skilled worker. For example, Rose *et al.* (1991) reported that 34% of people referred to an intensive case management service had been victims of childhood sexual abuse. This issue had not been adequately addressed through their prior contact with services.

It seems likely that the Department of Health (1990) recommendations for case management apply better to client groups other than those with severe and long-term mental health problems. For example, if the client group is relatively stable and easy to reach (e.g. frail older people) the case manager may need to engage in less personal contact, concentrating instead on carrying out periodic reviews and coordinating service inputs.

Integrating case management and direct-care tasks contributed to high morale within the EIS. This was certainly true in the case of the community mental health nurses who had all worked as ward or day hospital-based nurses before, and clearly enjoyed the greater responsibility and autonomy that case management bestowed. When case managers are higher up the managerial hierarchy, direct-care staff may experience a reduction in autonomy, as they find themselves coordinated from above. While some may value this, particularly if it results in demonstrable improvements for users, others may feel devalued by it. We can be sure, however, that giving direct-care staff greater responsibility is dangerous when it is not accompanied by correspondingly increased support, training and supervision.

WHAT CONTROL SHOULD CASE MANAGERS HAVE OVER RESOURCE ALLOCATION?

This question is inextricably linked with the purchaser-provider split and the division of health and social services respon- sibilities embodied within the NHS and Community Care Act (1990) (Chapter 2). Although the community care white paper (Cm 849, 1989) recommended that social service departments become the lead agency for social care, there remains con- siderable leeway for negotiation or dispute over respective responsibilities. Definitions of health and social care and their implications for funding are likely to be determined locally, along with local authorities' criteria for eligibility for assess- ment. Since resources for community care have not been ring- fenced, people with continuing mental health service needs will compete with other local authority priorities (e.g. child care). Great variability in users' access to resources is likely, and skilled and energetic advocates will be needed more than ever.

Caring for People is ambiguous about whether budgets should be seen as a necessary part of the case manager's role. Some case management systems (e.g. Kent Social Services) give case managers the job of coordinating all the available resources for service inputs to meet user need. Case managers have the job of coordinating an assessment and then purchasing services from a menu of available services. It is argued that placing the power to buy services close to users increases flexibility and the efficient use of resources. However, conflicts of interest may arise. It is unrealistic for the case manager to act as both the user's advocate and rationer of services. Since each role pulls expenditure in opposite directions, it is untenable to be simul- taneously accountable for both. The problem is exacerbated if the case manager carries responsibility for case-finding. Managing a limited budget acts as a clear disincentive to finding further people with needs to drain it unless funds are allocated on a strictly per capita basis. Budget-holding may also decrease flexibility if case managers know that they have only a limited array of choices on offer. This will reduce the assessment to an exercise in establishing the user's eligibility for pre-determined packages of care.

As there is an inevitable tension between service rationing, and advocacy and identification, the most logical approach may be to place each function within separate management hierarchies or separate organizations. The Holyoke/Chicopee case management service (Chapter 3) exemplifies a system in which assessment and resource rationing are kept completely separate so that the case manager is unfettered and able to perform a genuine assessment of need.

There is also a middle course, as demonstrated in the Thanet, Darlington and Maidstone Community Care Projects where case managers managed a limited budget for the purchase of minor items such as domestic appliances and assistance from informal carers (Challis and Davies, 1986; Knapp et al., 1991). The budget was not used for the gross buying-in of services from pre-set menus. This partial devolution of control to case managers may increase their motivation to manage resources flexibly and promote individual initiative. Since the options are not pre-determined, it may also stimulate the market of local service suppliers thereby increasing the diversity of service provision. Furthermore, acting as broker for a flexible range of services may motivate case managers to develop their knowledge of local resources (Hadley and McGrath, 1984). Such partial devolution of resource control to the periphery is likely to foster independence on the part of the case management service, and so may achieve some of the advantages of autonomy. However, paradoxically, devolution also requires tight central control over the means to ensuring high quality and efficiency (Vass, 1990).

IS CASE MANAGEMENT A JOB OR A SET OF TASKS?

Should case management be a specialist job designation or a set of tasks that can be integrated into normal working practice? The EIS had a traditional community mental health team (CMHT) format whereby each team member retained a professional identity and role while also taking on case management responsibility. Inevitably, this led to a blurring of roles and case management tasks competing with more usual professional functions. The psychologist is in the unfamiliar position of helping people with their social security benefits and the consultant psychiatrist phones the housing department in order to get someone re-housed in an emergency. On the other hand, the fact that one person is responsible for a range of tasks increases continuity and promotes accurate and continuous communication with users and others involved.

The alternative is to create a new discipline of case management whereby case managers come from a range of professional backgrounds, or indeed no professional background at all, and are trained in case management. Non-professional workers have been shown to be effective in a number of contexts (Milne *et al.*, 1989; Huxley, 1990) and may offer the significant advantage of sharing the user's social and cultural background. They may also be more familiar with local services and more likely to do the practical legwork necessary to ensure successful linkage (Dill, 1987). Furthermore, their selection and training can be more specifically tailored to the requirements of the job. The Denver Citywide Program, for example, selected young people who were disillusioned with the traditional practice of psychiatry on the assumption that they would be more committed to pursuing a radical alternative. The introduction of National Vocational Qualifications in Britain may make it easier for non-professionals to acquire a range of relevant skills through completing specific modules, thereby increasing access for people with valuable life experience (Morrish, 1988). In particular, users of mental health services are likely to have much to offer (Chapter 11).

There are, however, potential disadvantages to specialized non-professional case management. Practitioners may be unfamiliar with the labyrinthine nature of health, welfare and social service systems and the guerrilla activity that is often required to achieve desired outcomes. Depending on the demands of the role, it may also be important that the case manager has their own professional skills and expertise to call upon. One cornerstone of professionalism is knowing when the demands of a task exceed the limits of personal and professional competence and when another worker should be brought in. In some cases users may benefit from being safeguarded by professional codes of practice and clear accountability.

SHOULD CASE MANAGERS BE BASED IN HOSPITALS OR IN THE COMMUNITY?

Case management is so strongly identified with community care that it may seem odd to consider basing it in hospitals. However, there are some arguments for considering this option. Many users may be in need of help because of inadequate planning and linkage to support when discharged from hospital. Problems often arise in establishing a relationship between agencies across the divide between hospital and community. They operate within different systems of care, with different funding and authority structures. Hospital-based care is often identified with an overly biological and treatment-orientated philosophy of care, while hospital-based workers, often with equal justification, consider community-based services to be tinkering in the margins of mental health care with little consideration of those most in need.

Experience at the EIS, which at different times operated from both locations, confirmed that it is more difficult to link with community agencies from within a hospital. However, this may not be a universal experience. Hospital-based teams have advantages. There is ready access to medical and other professional input for assessment and planning and some community-based agencies, such as the police and social services departments, are already orientated towards contacting the hospital when they encounter someone who seems significantly crazy. Moreover, positive results have been reported from hospital-based programmes aimed at linking users to services at discharge. Methods include continuing therapy on an out-patient basis with a hospital worker, establishing direct contact between hospital workers and community-based staff, pre-discharge interviews to provide information about community-based alternatives, offering pre-discharge sessions with community-based workers and establishing a discharge referral coordinator (Axelrod and Wetzler, 1989). Altman (1983) found that over one year, a programme that arranged aftercare before discharge had rehospitalization rates three times lower than those of control group users. Axelrod and Wetzler (1989) found that users' compliance with aftercare was associated with fewer days between discharge and the first scheduled aftercare appointment. Improvement was also associated with the number of prior hospitalizations and longer lengths of stay in the hospital which suggests that this effect is not limited to those who are able to stay out of hospital anyway.

The critical feature in these studies appears to be continuity of care (Rosenfield *et al.*, 1986); a central feature of case management. Ideally this should not depend on the location of case management services. As users live in communities it seems most appropriate that their primary link to mental health service providers should be based there too. This promotes earlier intervention, avoids assuming the prevailing culture of the institution and creates opportunities for avoiding the deleterious effects of admission (Lipton *et al.*, 1981). Ideally, community-based case managers should be able to follow users in and out of hospital care, while retaining responsibility for coordinating their support. Unfortunately medical authority often precludes such arrangements and admission to hospital usually requires wholesale transfer of responsibility to a hospital-based consultant. This is perhaps the most significant bull that policy-makers have yet to take by the horns. The apportioning of responsibility between consultant and case manager remains unclear. The best solution, as suggested by Kanter (1989), may be for consultants to remain responsible for biological interventions while case managers concern themselves with environmental manipulations. For this to work effectively, there would need to be agreement over what constitutes an environmental manipulation. Discharge would logically come under this heading, although clearly this would require amendment of the Mental Health Act (1983) to give powers of admission and discharge to case managers. Their powers would need to be similar to those of approved social workers and they would need to be advised by medical staff over the user's mental state. Psychologists are already seeking admission rights in parts of the US (Jabitsky, 1988).

Since continuity of care largely depends on the relations between hospitals and community agencies (Rosenfield *et al.*, 1986), service planners need to assess the local situation and consider from which location case managers may best contribute to continuity of care, and what formal arrangements are needed to bolster their authority when liaising with other agencies.

WHICH AGENCY SHOULD MANAGE CASE MANAGERS?

A core feature of the *Caring for People* recommendations was the distinction between health and social care as the basis for the funding of health and social services. It is easy, if rather tautologous, to define health care as that which health care professions provide: for example, nursing care, medical treatment and acute admissions. Social care can then be defined as all the rest.

This might, for example, give rise to the service configuration shown in Figure 4.2. Here, referrals for health care are made to a health care agency such as a CMHT while referrals for social care go to local authority-managed case managers. However, many health authority staff provide significant social and psychological support in addition to their health care tasks. Nursing, physiotherapy, speech therapy, occupational therapy and clinical psychology all encompass skills beyond the realm of medicine and it is nonsensical to restrict their role to traditional health care tasks. Most importantly, the majority of people with long-term mental health problems have need of both health and social care over long and sometimes continuous periods. In the configuration shown in Figure 4.2 this blend of health and social care provision would need to be achieved through cross-referral or contracting arrangements between the CMHT and the case managers. The referrers have the difficult task of determining where to refer and for what, and may find themselves having to make arbitrary distinctions about whether the users' health or social care needs predominate.

A rational jointly-managed alternative is shown in Figure 4.3, whereby all referrals are made to a single team which has within it personnel fulfilling case management functions. All team members would be professionally accountable to their line managers in the health and local authority in the usual way, and in addition, are accountable for a certain level of resource expenditure to a joint board of health and local authority managers. This line of accountability may be via a team coordinator allowing a single point of contact between the team and the joint board. The joint board would be responsible for a budget and the team may petition it for further resources. Thus resource rationing remains a management function.

Joint boards also allow the potential for health and local

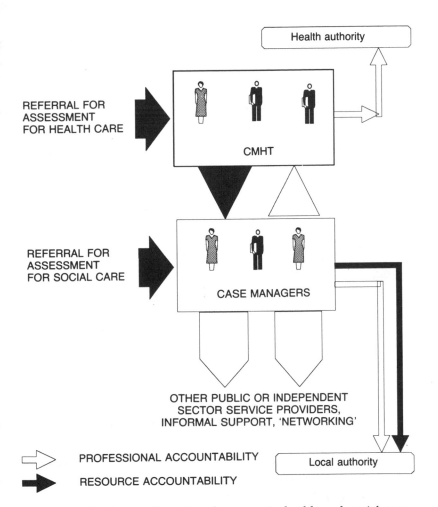

Figure 4.2 Service configuration for separate health and social care referral.

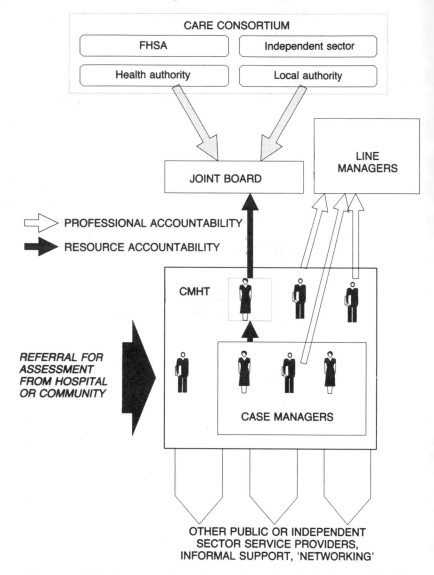

Figure 4.3 Jointly managed service configuration for integrated health and social care referral.

authorities to join with other agencies, such as family health service authorities and independent sector agencies, to pool resources and thereby increase flexibility and continuity of provision. Lead agency status in developing community care initiatives powerfully determines the culture and practice of developments (Knapp *et al.*, 1991). Forming care consortia by bringing together a mix of service commissioners from both the statutory and independent sectors allows a clean slate on which to design needs and values-led services. This may also create opportunities for good practice, such as local community and service user representation on management groups.

Other likely service configurations are:

1. Health authority-managed multidisciplinary teams of case managers with a health care coordinating role in addition to their normal practice. Social care resources would be sought through liaison with local authority-managed case managers.
2. Health authority-managed multidisciplinary teams of case managers with a specific role in case-finding and assessment. They would have formal links with local authority resource managers who coordinate and resource social care. This approach devolves the difficult decision-making entailed in defining social care to the clinical team and risks dividing up the core case management tasks.
3. Local authority-managed teams of experienced social workers with case manager responsibilities. Their main role is in assessment and service brokerage, and they may manage other staff. They are responsible for managing a limited budget that can be used to buy in other services.
4. Care consortia-managed teams including professional and non-professional staff selected on a very specific range of differing criteria (e.g. ability to speak certain minority languages, or experience in establishing work projects). Small budgets may be devolved according to needs as they arise.
5. Health or local authority-managed case managers operating independently of CMHTs, and sometimes with a devolved budget. This appears to be a popular proposal but often lacks consideration of identification, accountability

relationships to provider agencies and personnel, and staff support issues.
6. Independent teams of specialist case managers operating in parallel with CMHTs with a specific role in assessment or advocacy. Rather than having any buying power, they rely on assertive petitioning and negotiation for services.

SHOULD CASE MANAGERS WORK IN TEAMS?

There are few examples of individual case managers working in isolation. Nonetheless, there is some dispute about whether the process of case management can be a function of the team as a whole. For example, although the Holyoke/Chicopee case managers were formed into teams, they stressed that case management itself was not a team function and that responsibility for the core tasks of case management rested with named individuals (Smith, 1990b). This is so for any model of case management where the relationship between the user and the case manager is paramount (Rapp and Wintersteen, 1989; Miller, 1983). A contrary conclusion was drawn by Bond *et al.* (1988) who found that a team where case loads were assigned to individual workers rather than shared among the team as a whole was less effective in keeping users out of hospital, involved the users in less overall contact and increased the burden on individual workers.

Whatever the arrangements for allocating case loads, there are potential advantages in organizing case managers into teams. These include the pooling of skills, knowledge and experience and the provision of mutual support and peer supervision. Teams are able to build a resource of information and experience that outlives the period of employment of any one individual worker. The formation of teams that are self-generating and internally supportive may also provide a useful vehicle for innovation within reactionary systems (Georgiades and Phillimore, 1975; Chapter 11). Organizing services into relatively autonomous units generally increased the quality of care by increasing the time spent in contact with users, and promoting user-centred planning (Watts and Bennett, 1983).

However, multidisciplinary teamwork is not without its

fair share of potential pitfalls. Beardshaw and Towell (1990) identified problems such as reluctance among team members to share skills, a lack of consensus about the purpose of assessment, overcomplicated administrative procedures, a focus on service resources rather than need, concentration on user weaknesses rather than strengths, inadequate involvement of users and carers, and lack of consensus about monitoring and review arrangements. However, these criticisms could be made of services *per se*. Considering them as inherent to multidisciplinary teams probably means throwing the baby out with the bath water. Indeed, a central argument of this book is that teams may offer a managerial framework for working to improve the practice of service providers in these areas.

CONCLUSIONS

Ten conclusions about case management systems can be drawn from Part One.

1. The purpose of case management systems must be clear, particularly over priorities for resource allocation.
2. Case management cannot be tacked onto existing structures. It demands a radical re-think of systems for securing provision from the bottom up. Decisions about the integration of case management with existing providers, the devolution of responsibility for case management tasks to direct-care staff, whether case management should be a specific job designation, and where the service should undertake most of its work are inextricably linked to the assessed needs of the target client group and the degree to which they are being met by existing local service provision.
3. Responsibility for case management cannot be shared around. The task of offering case management to a defined population must rest with a single agency at local level, although ideally that agency will be jointly commissioned.
4. The core tasks of case management, (assessment, planning, implementation, monitoring and review) should

not be split up. The case manager is responsible for the well-being of the user at all times regardless of their engagement with other agencies.

5. Case managers are usually workers with accountability to management hierarchies. As such they are not in a position to offer vociferous and unfettered advocacy for users. This is particularly so if they are managing resources. Case managers need to ensure that users are able to access advocates outside of service-providing systems.

6. Unbiased assessment of unmet need by case managers is made easier if they are not given responsibility for resource rationing and have a minimal role in service provision.

7. Case management systems offer a vehicle for monitoring the delivery and quality of service inputs.

8. A case management system should be outcome-orientated. The aim is not to provide a service but to help users achieve better outcomes.

9. Case managers organized into semi-autonomous units commissioned by care consortia of service providers may offer the best opportunity for rational pooling of resources and shared vision.

10. Whatever their role, case managers must receive adequate training, back-up and support from their organization in order to ensure continuous high-quality services and avoid staff burn-out.

It is possible to develop organizational frameworks for case management that meet the needs of users, carers and workers. Part Two will consider the practice of case management within such a system.

Part Two

The Practice of Case Management

Chapter 5

Principles of practice

Much of what has been described in Part One will be behind the scenes as far as users and carers are concerned. However a service is designed, it comes to nothing if practice at face-to-face level is of poor quality, particularly since one-to-one contact is often all users experience of a case management system.

SIX PRINCIPLES OF PRACTICE

Good practice is inevitably based upon a clear statement of guiding principles. Rapp and Wintersteen (1989) describe six general principles as the basis of their approach. Although the following discussion is a synthesis of various views on case management, it employs their overall framework.

Focus on individual strengths rather than pathology

Psychiatry is the practice of medicine applied to mental health. While it is widely recognized that psychiatry has a role to play in the alleviation of symptoms of mental disorder, a medical approach to assessment and subsequent intervention does not accord with the social, environmental and political nature of mental health. The 'medical model' is not just about prescribing drugs. It is an approach to working with people, and conceptualizing their problems. What the worker sees and what the user tells them about the way they feel are, in medical terms, 'signs and symptoms'. Working on the medical model, this information is distilled into a diagnosis. A diagnosis is thus most accurately considered a summary description of those signs and symptoms. Treatment is a method selected on the basis of the diagnosis. How useful is this process?

The label 'agoraphobia' offers an example. Most clinical psychologists will be familiar with medical referrals that go something along the lines of, 'Ms X is a long-standing agoraphobic who has not responded to minor tranquillizers. I would be grateful if you would see her with a view to putting her through a desensitization programme.' The doctor has been presented with someone who may feel depressed, devalued, unable to cope, anxious in public places, breathless, concerned about dying or illness, unsupported by her husband, persecuted by her children and demanding of a cure. The process of diagnosis parcels up these signs and symptoms under the heading 'agoraphobia' for despatch to another worker. On receipt of the parcel, a worker operating on a medical model would apply the treatment of choice as requested. However, any worker not working on a medical model has the job of unpacking the diagnosis in order to find out what is actually going on. Diagnosis is a neat way of creating order out of chaos, but cannot represent the experience of the user. Of all the many people I have worked with who have been labelled agoraphobic, I cannot think of two that could be said to have the same problem. The diagnostic process has been strongly criticized for its lack of reliability and predictive power (Scheff, 1985; Bentall, 1990). It often wastes time when it would be better simply to describe what people are doing and experiencing.

Diagnosis is also problematic because it affects the way we think. It subtly legitimizes our neglect of social and environmental causes of poor mental health. This is particularly so when it is used not just as a description but as an explanation: Ms X is breathless and anxious *because* she is agoraphobic. This soon gets very circular. How do we know she is agoraphobic? Because she is breathless. Why is she breathless? Because she is agoraphobic. Neat but unhelpful.

Worse still, users become identified with their diagnoses. Ms X *is* an agoraphobic. Perhaps this is because in company with diabetics, asthmatics, arthritics, bronchitics and lepers, the diagnosis tends to last a long time. In mental health this is unsurprising, not least because of the continuity of social environments that maintain poor mental health. However

Rosenhan (1973), in a famous and controversial study, showed how labels are inherently sticky. He found that following the admission of confederates to hospital (on the basis of their claiming to hear voices) their behaviour was interpreted as symptomatic of their supposed illness. Despite acting totally normally, they found it very difficult to get discharged from hospital, and even when they did many were still labelled 'schizophrenic in remission'. It is perhaps unsurprising amidst such expectations that people find themselves assuming roles that accord with their diagnosis. The assumption of such a role can also be a way of regulating stress and avoiding situations of which users may be fearful. In this way, diagnosis exploits the most handicapping aspects of poor mental health.

A counter argument in favour of diagnosis is often encountered from carers (notably the National Schizophrenia Fellowship). They have argued that a failure on the part of psychiatrists to make a firm diagnosis leaves relatives in ignorance and makes it more difficult for the 'sufferer' to get help. This is lamentably true but says more about the central role given to diagnosis as the basis for planning and delivering services than it does about its intrinsic merits.

Case managers should be trained to see strengths and skills rather than focusing wholly on liabilities and deficits. This is not to neglect the very real handicaps that can accompany and exacerbate mental health problems. It simply makes the user an active participant in shaping their own destiny through deploying, resurrecting or developing skills or other assets within them and their environments. Aside from being a more constructive approach to assessment, it is in itself more therapeutic. For people who may already have low self-esteem and a highly self-punishing way of interpreting experience, it is unlikely to be helpful to start by parading their deficiencies, abnormalities and failures before them. Furthermore, focusing on strengths goes some way towards being a constant reminder to workers that they are collaborating with a whole person with unique qualities rather than a rag-bag of problems to be 'treated' and infantilized. Whole people demand respect, dignity, choice and a level of assistance that meets their needs while maintaining their autonomy.

The case manager-user relationship is primary and essential

A professional relationship between the user and the case manager must be established in which they become real people to each other. Intagliata (1982) states that the 'most influential aspect of the case management process is the quality of personal commitment that the case managers develop towards their clients' (p. 660). This is very different from pure brokerage models in which the relationship between case manager and user may consist of an impersonal series of transactions aimed at accomplishing specific ends.

Although the relationship between the case manager and user is of paramount importance, the relationship between them is not 'normal' in the way that one might have a relationship with a friend, relative or colleague. Case managers are always in a position of power over users and it is dangerous to neglect this. Good and professional practice is about recognizing this power and avoiding its abuse by making the relationship as collaborative as possible.

The centrality of the user-case manager relationship ensures that help is reliably available and accessible to users and carers. Miller (1983) argues that a case management system must offer all the core tasks of case management to users regardless of their engagement with other agencies who may themselves be doing case manager-like activities. The case manager is responsible for the well-being of the user at all times and there is no buck-passing. The word 'referral' in case management only has a very qualified meaning, and does not usually imply the transfer of responsibility for the overall welfare of users. The exercise of this principle is clearly easier when the case manager undertakes some of the tasks of a primary worker (e.g. doing family work, skills training or individual counselling).

Interventions are based on the principle of user self-determination

The principle of self-determination should not be confused with the 1980s culture of individualism, or the human potential movement of the 1970s (Rosen, 1977). It is not assumed that anyone can be what they want to be if only they take responsibility for themselves and their lives. This too easily equates with blaming victims of enduring social inequalities for their own disadvantages.

Self-determination is concerned with maximizing the power of users and carers in decision-making concerning their lives, ensuring that they are able to exercise choice wherever possible and developing a collaborative approach to the core tasks of case management. Users set the agenda as far as possible and the work should be focused on objectives derived from their needs, goals and aspirations. As Rapp and Wintersteen (1989) put it, the case manager 'supports and sustains the client in the process of securing the needed resources, only intervening directly when this is in the long-term best interest of the client' (p. 26). This latter point cannot be ducked. There may be times when the case manager has to act for users but against their will. The obvious example is when individuals are about to become a danger to themselves or others and the case manager has to arrange a formal assessment for their removal to a more controlling environment (such as an acute ward if no better alternative exists). The aim of continuous and in-depth involvement with users is to stop such situations arising. However, such events are sometimes unavoidable and users should have access to an independent advocate who will safeguard their interests. Although the case manager should be working on behalf of users, ultimately they lack the independence from service systems necessary for advocacy work, particularly if they hold budgetary or resource-rationing responsibilities. Nonetheless, case managers do have a role in helping the user identify an advocate to act on their behalf. Self-determination on the part of users is a valid and attainable goal in case management and is not negated by the uneven power relationship between user and case manager.

Assertive outreach is the preferred mode of intervention

Those most in need of services are usually the last people to turn up at an out-patient department asking for help. Studies looking at follow-up appointments following discharge show very disappointing attendance (Dowell and Ciarlo, 1983; Huxley, 1990). Very disturbed or distressed people do not tend to walk into drop-in services spontaneously. In general, such services serve only very local areas and quickly become identified with a particular user stereotype to the exclusion of others. Reasons for drop-out or non-attendance include disaffection with mental health services, memory impairments, difficulties structuring time, communication problems, lack of information and stigmatizing, inaccessible, unwelcoming or culturally insensitive services (Hagan, 1990).

Aside from the practical and cost implications of missed appointment times, there are good reasons for taking services to where users spend most time. A more valid assessment can be achieved through meeting them in context and maximizing the involvement of other important people. The EIS particularly focused attention on isolated young mothers living in temporary bed-and-breakfast accommodation in inner London. Witnessing the conditions under which these women were having to look after themselves and their children made the assessment of their situation far more relevant. It also gave the team credibility with health visitors who were already providing valuable input, and promoted joint working. The EIS also worked with long-stay residents in local authority hostels. This allowed the team to involve their keyworkers in assessment and subsequent action, vastly increasing continuity and support.

Seeing users at home also helps to keep control with them. They are in the role of host and so are in a position to offer something back to the case manager. This promotes an informal and collaborative tenor to the work and helps build their sense of self-worth.

Chapter three described many examples of services that have shown positive outcomes arising from assertive outreach. With a shift towards community-based care, early intervention and crisis intervention, this can no longer be seen as a luxurious or specialist mode of service provision.

People with long-term and severe mental health problems can continue to learn, grow and change and can be assisted to do so

There is a considerable literature on the positive outcome of interventions with people who have long-term and severe

problems, even those who have been damaged through institutional care (e.g. Liberman *et al.*, 1986; Tarrier, 1991).
However, this principle is as much about attitude as it is about
outcome studies. Recent textbooks on family therapy (e.g.
Carpenter and Treacher, 1989) have emphasized the influence
of Milton Erickson and his followers (such as Jay Haley)
on therapists' perspectives on change. Whereas traditional
systems theory was essentially a theory of no change or
homoeostasis, these writers viewed change as inevitable and
ongoing. Instead of a therapist asking, 'Tell me if anything
changes between now and next week', they are more inclined
to ask the users to 'Note those changes that occur over the next
week that you wish to keep happening as part of your life'. In
part, this reiterates the need to focus on strengths rather than
deficits. In addition, it underlines the belief that individuals
are inextricable, active parts of systems that cannot help but
change with changing circumstances. What appears to be
resistance or stubborn refusal to change is in fact an action
towards a certain way of behaving in a certain circumstance.
The aim is to work with the user and their circumstances to tilt
the balance towards the achievement of more positive, long-
term outcomes.

Steps, no matter how small, that lead towards a user-selected
goal are themselves goals to be reinforced upon their accomplishment. In this way achievements are consolidated and
users begin to realize their own potential for changing their
environment and their role within it. Perceiving and building
on these barely perceptible increments is one of the core
competences of case management.

Resource acquisition goes beyond traditional mental health services and actively mobilizes resources for the entire community. Community is defined as a resource and not as an obstacle

Part of the labelling process described above involves segregating people with service histories by structuring their lives
around a menu of mental health service provision. Here again
it is important to consider the function of services for people.
Does someone need day care (provided by a day centre or a
day hospital) or do they need something meaningful to do

during the day? Davis (1990) has given a trenchant account of users' perceptions of the benefits of day care. Very rarely did treatment get a mention. People appreciated the opportunity to escape from the four walls of home to talk informally with others. The most valued contacts were with other service users rather than staff, who were often perceived as too busy, particularly in treatment-orientated facilities managed by health authorities. The opportunity to save on heating bills, access to phones, washing and laundry facilities and food were also valued. Case managers need to think less in terms of linking users to service provision and more towards meeting need in whatever way is most attractive to users. This often involves linking with ordinary facilities used by the rest of the community, such as libraries, cafes, and sports facilities. Communities are resources for employment, social involvement and recreation. One of the most demanding skills of case management is working with community members in order to help users find a valued place among them.

SAFEGUARDING THE RIGHTS OF USERS

The power relationships between service providers and users cannot be over-emphasized. A central feature of case management is the devolution of greater amounts of responsibility to individual workers. This responsibility often encompasses influence over major aspects of the user's life such as access to accommodation, money, employment, and social and leisure opportunities. Case managers may even influence people's access to basic medical care. The potential for abuse of this power is enormous. For this reason it is important that case management only occurs within organizations that can regulate and monitor its practice. Responsibility for ensuring users' rights does not just lie with the system, however. The individual worker also needs to be aware of their own potential to abuse and maintain an awareness of the fundamental human rights of service users.

Wolowitz (1983) has argued that increases in social services have correlated with decreases in user autonomy. Although their motives were benevolent and the ends worthy, liberal service providers were blind to the effect of their largesse on service users. They assumed the posture of parents and completely failed to resist the urge to establish dominion over people's lives. This resulted in infantilized users denied their rights. However, at the other extreme, the case manager cannot be an unwitting agent of the users' will. Kanter (1985) states that '. . . the existence of case managers is based upon the premise that chronic psychiatric patients are unable to manage their own affairs' (p. 84). This is only partly true. More than anything, case management is based upon the experience that services are unable to manage *themselves* effectively. Nonetheless, it is true that if users were totally able to manage their lives, there would be no need for case management.

The complete autonomy of users remains the goal of service provision rather than the workaday reality. Case managers are therefore faced with a conflict over their responsibilities for managing cases and the need to avoid disempowering service users. This conflict cannot be solved and parcelled away. It requires constant attention to maximizing the users' access to information and the opportunity for them to exercise choice within the boundaries of law.

Users need to know what it means to be case-managed. That includes an honest account of the situations in which the case manager may need to act against their will. Once this is understood, people may wish to exercise the right not to be case-managed. This has to be respected. Individuals have the right to be abnormal, and to act in crazy ways. This may mean them being offensive, intimidating or a burden to carers. As long as they are not assessed as being a danger to themselves or other people (under the terms of the Mental Health Act 1983) people are quite within their rights to be left completely alone.

If users refuse case management this should affect their access to services as little as possible, and appropriate referrals elsewhere should be made. If users agree to case management, feedback and complaints procedures within the organization should be established, publicized and maintained.

Case managers have access to considerable knowledge about users through assessment and their continuing involvement. For this reason they need to pay particular attention to the user's right to privacy. This is particularly salient to the case manager's linking and coordinating functions. In the US there is a fundamental right of personal privacy which the US Supreme Court has elevated to a constitutional principle. Wolowitz (1983) described three principles when sharing information with a third party:

1. No information should be released without the informed consent of the user or their legal representative.
2. Only the minimum amount of information necessary to achieve the desired purpose should be released, and only to the appropriate parties, and
3. Recipients of information should not be allowed to share the information with other agencies or persons.

Users should exercise informed consent when authorizing the release of privileged information which in turn requires their access to records so that they know what is being conveyed, the identity of the person receiving the information and why they are receiving it.

In Britain, information that the user shares with the case manager becomes the property of the employing authority. It can therefore be shared within that organization. The relevant authorities are given considerable discretionary powers in deciding how this information is to be used. Nonetheless, Wolowitz's principles represent good practice and case managers have an obligation not to divulge information that could cause the user harm unless there is an overriding need to do so in the public interest. Should the issue of confidentiality arise, case managers should make clear the limits on their ability to keep secrets.

CONCLUSION

These principles of practice shape the relationship between user and case manager and determine many of the tasks that case managers will undertake. They create a demand for case managers to be open and honest in their communication with users and require a particular set of values, beliefs and attitudes about work with people with severe and long-term mental health problems.

The next three chapters will examine how these principles translate into the practice of case management.

Chapter 6

Tasks of case management I – the initial phase

A FRAMEWORK FOR THE TASKS OF CASE MANAGEMENT

The framework shown in Figure 6.1 shows the tasks that can be encompassed within a case management role that is as inclusive as possible while maintaining a coherent role for case managers. All the tasks shown can be undertaken by one team of case managers (all but brokerage were performed by the EIS) although the emphasis given to certain tasks will depend on the particular approach adopted. The tasks undertaken should be influenced by the needs of the local population and the availability and collaboration of local services. For example, the case management service may be able to refer to other agencies for crisis intervention, family therapy, skills training, individual therapy or drug therapy, without risking discontinuity.

Figure 6.1 separates an initial phase of contact from interventions that focus on work with the user's environment, the user themselves, and the interrelation between the user and their environment. This classification of tasks reflects their emphasis only, since all case management tasks are concerned with the interrelationships between users and their social and physical environments to some degree. The arrows of Figure 6.1 emphasize that the tasks of case management are rarely undertaken sequentially, except during the initial phase. Usually the case manager is undertaking several tasks at the same time.

This chapter concentrates on the tasks undertaken during the initial phase: engagement, relationship building, assessment and planning. Although these tasks must be performed first, they never completely cease during the user's

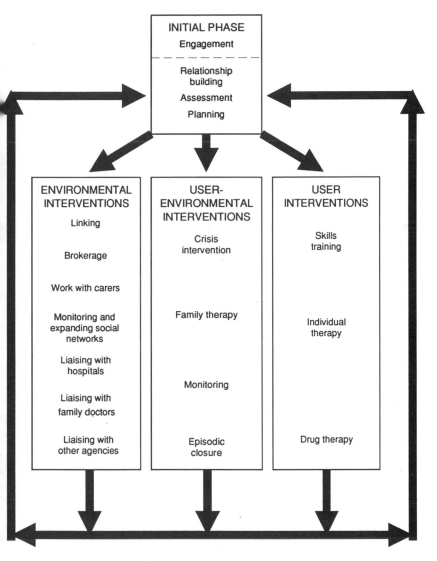

Figure 6.1 The tasks of case management.

involvement with the case management service. All case management activity should serve to build the case manager's relationship with the user and inform ongoing assessment and planning.

ENGAGEMENT

Very few people seek help from mental health services with enthusiasm. Case managers are usually offering a service to people who are under some pressure to accept help. At best, they may have been sent by another worker, such as a family doctor, or by a relative, friend or colleague. At worst, they are frankly hostile, having been singled out for unwanted attention. The EIS received many calls from social workers and housing workers who had been contacted by residents or landlords over people creating disturbances in or around their own homes. Typically, this involved bizarre or intimidating behaviour that was liable to result in imminent eviction. The case manager in this situation has the job of establishing contact with someone who initially has no interest in having any relationship with services and can see no benefit from it.

As in any relationship, first impressions are very important. The following are some guidelines for engagement that aim to maximize the chances of achieving a sound foundation on which to base a helping relationship, while simultaneously ensuring that the autonomy and rights of users are not infringed.

Be prepared

As much information as possible should be collected before arranging the first meeting. The aim of information collection at this stage is to establish the optimum conditions for the formation of a relationship. The case manager needs to establish the best place to meet the user for the first time, who else to involve and how to present the help on offer. It is important to know about the user's attitude to receiving help, who else is likely to be around if they are visited at home and whether it will be helpful to involve them.

The best source of information are users themselves. The

only exceptions are when the initial referral suggests that there may be particular problems in establishing a relationship with them. The case manager may then wish to contact other health and social services personnel with past or present involvement. The first stop when collecting this information is normally the referrer.

The EIS began collecting information for planning of assessment from the point of referral using a registration form. The case manager had the job of filling in any important gaps in information collected from the referrer before meeting the user for the first time.

Attend to issues of difference

It is important to consider whether there are aspects of the worker that will alienate users, for example due to differences in race, gender or perceived class. In some cases, they may be known to react very negatively towards certain types of people, for example men. While exposure to these people might be a valid mutual objective at a later stage, when meeting for the first time it is important to take these preferences into account. It is also necessary to establish whether any communication problems may arise and if an interpreter is needed.

Make yourself a real person who has come from somewhere

This means stating who you are, where you are from and how you come to be making the approach. As a case manager you are presenting yourself as a stranger coming out of nowhere. The user needs to be able to place you in some context. Normally, this will be done by letter or phone before visiting. This initial contact usually includes an invitation to ask other people to be there when the case manager and user meet for the first time.

Where possible, contact by phone to make the initial appointment has the advantages of a more immediate exchange of information, direct re-assurance and explanation, and negotiation about the timing and location of the first visit.

It is only admissible to omit giving prior warning of a visit if past attempts at engagement have shown that the user will avoid contact if it is arranged beforehand. It is still important for the case manager to introduce themselves properly. This may seem obvious but it is surprising how easy it is to forget such details and then find oneself wondering why the user was reluctant to speak to someone who was shouting up from the street about 'just wanting to talk'.

The case manager should start by introducing themselves by name rather than by job designation. Aside from being polite, it is easier to slam the door in the social worker's face than it is in Jane's, or Tom's. It is important to be honest but tactful. Shouting up that you are from the local mental health team may get the user running to the door out of sheer embarrassment but is not recommended as an engagement strategy. On the other hand, pretending to be the gasman will do nothing to establish a collaborative relationship once you are inside and have to come clean.

It is rarely helpful to introduce oneself as a mental health worker at the outset. For many people this carries alarming implications concerning drugs, hospital or psychotherapy. Although these may be features of the work, it is more likely that the focus will be on tackling everyday problems. For this reason it is not dishonest to introduce oneself as being there to help solve problems. It can be helpful to describe the service by giving examples of the sort of work it does with people who have problems similar to the user.

The case manager must describe why they are visiting at this particular time. This often means saying who it was that contacted the service. Occasionally this is a bad idea if the user is known to despise them. The EIS was often contacted when all else had failed and so began with a recent history of hostile encounters with other workers. It is also important to be aware of not exposing neighbours, relatives or friends to persecution by the user for having made a referral.

Get alongside the user

Sometimes after the case manager has offered help, the user denies problems. The user may feel alienated, angry and frightened and the case manager is yet another problem to overcome. The case manager must communicate that they are there to help the user, rather than as an agent for other people. Often the best way of achieving this is to begin problem-solving on issues that the user is presenting there and then. It can be helpful to check with the user information received from the referrer, construing it in terms of the personal and practical implications for the user. It makes more sense to talk about the danger of being thrown out of a hotel for making too much noise at night than it does to get straight into discussions about being persecuted by auditory hallucinations.

Show respect

The case manager is there to offer a service to the user and this should be reflected in the initial contact. They should, if possible, find out beforehand how the user prefers to be addressed. First name terms should not be assumed. Aside from issues of etiquette, for many people it may be positively disorientating. There is no therapeutic basis for ever assuming a flippant, abusive or confrontational manner when first meeting users.

Another way of showing respect is to listen carefully to what the user is saying, and avoid the assumption that their account is being distorted by craziness. One of the EIS users had a history of persecutory delusions and with the help of the EIS had been transferred to new accommodation because she was convinced that neighbours were constantly talking about her and listening behind the walls. Very soon after moving in to her new home, she began complaining that there was a child prostitution racket going on in the same building. This was interpreted as a relapse until a team member visited the user at home and came to the same conclusion. Many case managers are young and come from comparatively sheltered middle-class backgrounds. It becomes easy to mistake the unknown or unfamiliar for the impossible.

Establish links with individuals known and trusted by the user

Another way of helping the user to make sense of you is by approaching them with someone that they know and trust.

Often the user's family doctor is a good person to carry out an assessment with, and it may be helpful for them to introduce the case manager in the familiar setting of the general practice. However, this is not always possible and other solutions must be sought.

Mr X was a 40-year-old Iranian ex-soldier with no family contacts. He had intermittent involvement with the staff of a local voluntary drop-in centre who had referred him to the EIS because of his increasingly bizarre and paranoid behaviour. He was deemed intentionally homeless by the local authority following his eviction for non-payment of rent and had been living as a lodger in squalid conditions with someone who themselves experienced severe and long-term mental health problems. They rarely had gas or electricity and were disconnected at the time of referral. Mr X had been addicted to minor tranquillizers for some years and frequently changed his family practitioner in order to maintain a supply. He had recently collapsed on the street and was admitted to hospital. However, he discharged himself prematurely, fearing that the doctors were trying to kill him. Subsequently he had to be re-admitted in order to amputate part of his foot as a consequence of gangrene.

It was difficult to determine the best person to involve in a joint assessment since Mr X was indiscriminately paranoid and verbally aggressive. Following some investigation it was felt that, at that particular time, his strongest relationship was with the medical social worker who had been involved with Mr X since the amputation.

Mr V was a 22-year-old West Indian man referred by a hotel manager when the EIS visited to assess another user. The manager complained that Mr V was spitting at his television. He had been placed in bed-and-breakfast accommodation by an out-of-London borough who had lost his file and could offer no information on him. Mr V's only relationship appeared to be with a chambermaid who reported that he spat at the television because of his belief that people inside it were coming to get him. He was talking to himself in a manner that suggested he was hearing voices. For the past few weeks he had taken to his bed and, despite plenty of money lying around his room, he had not left the hotel to buy any food. In fact, he had only been kept alive by the kind attention of the chambermaid who had been slipping him food that she had obtained from elsewhere in the hotel.

Mr V's usual reaction to any approach was to spit. The chambermaid was instrumental in helping the assessors gain access to Mr V in order to attempt to communicate with him. He was found in a very poor physical condition and was almost too weak to leave his bed. It was impossible to communicate through his craziness and he had to be admitted to the local psychiatric unit for urgent assessment.

Persist where appropriate

Very often the user will reject an initial contact. In most cases this choice has to be respected and it is sometimes enough to leave a name and contact number in case they change their minds. Often, however, an impending crisis is all too apparent and the case manager should sensitively persist in attempting contact. It is usually helpful to maintain contact in a regular and predictable manner; calling at the same times and not producing any surprises. This allows the user to become familiar with the case manager in their own time. Ultimately however, the case manager must respect the right of the user not to accept help, even if the consequences look dire. The only exception would be where the user was a very real danger to themselves or others (as with Mr V above).

This case example illustrates a failure to engage:

Mrs P was a 49-year-old West Indian woman who had undergone a sudden personality change. She was becoming increasingly withdrawn and apathetic and spent most of her day lying on a sofa. She appeared to be hearing voices. Her dismayed husband had contacted the hospital, and the EIS was contacted after Mrs P had punched a consultant psychiatrist in the stomach as he attempted to assess her need for compulsory admission.

Mr P answered the phone when initial contact was made. As Mrs P would not come to the phone it was explained to her husband that the EIS were hoping to help her with whatever was concerning her and asked whether there was anything that would make it easier for her to see them. Mr P had no ideas but seemed keen that the EIS should assess the situation so a nurse and a psychologist visited.

They were met at the door by Mr P whereupon his wife made a bolt for the kitchen and barricaded herself in. In earshot of the kitchen they asked Mr P about why she had done this and reiterated that they were not there to take her into hospital, or force her to do anything against her will. They attempted to converse through the kitchen door, asking about whether it would be helpful for Mrs P to be seen elsewhere or whether there was someone else she would consider talking to. They received no replies. The rest of the session was spent talking to Mr P about the situation the family found themselves in, particularly trying to tease out any precipitating events. He was encouraged to contact the EIS if Mrs P felt able to talk to them, and arranged another appointment.

At the next session Mrs P retreated to the bedroom but did not barricade herself in. At subsequent meetings she lay on the sofa but would not communicate. Mr P, however, seemed to gain considerable benefit from the sessions, while their teenage children regarded the situation with wry amusement. After about six weeks of weekly visits during which Mr P reported increasingly bizarre behaviour and Mrs P lay on the sofa (latterly often deeply asleep), the EIS decided that the visits were not benefiting her and so terminated them, stressing to Mr P that he should contact them if Mrs P either got worse or improved.

Try another tack

Sometimes it needs to be acknowledged that the job of engagement should be given to someone else. There is no rule that says a case manager or user should like each other. Each may find aspects of the other's personality repellent. It should imply no loss of face to ask another colleague to work with a user, particularly if there are aspects of the worker that may bridge social or cultural gaps.

Alternatively, it may be useful to offer the user an appointment somewhere else. The user may be unable to state why they cannot discuss their difficulties within the household. Often, fear of abuse or ridicule makes it more difficult for people to seek help.

RELATIONSHIP BUILDING

Having laid the foundations of a positive relationship with the user, it then needs to be developed into an effective vehicle for collaborative working.

Be clear about what you can and cannot do

It is important that the user understands why you have arrived on the scene and what you can offer. This requires honesty on the part of case managers when explaining the limits of their powers to access resources, so that case manager and user can join together creatively to attempt to fill any gaps in provision.

With some people it may be necessary to describe the limitations of unquestioning support that the case manager can offer. The case manager obviously cannot support the user in any illegal acts and there are limits to the confidentiality that can be offered. We have already described how the case manager, while acting in the user's best interests, may have to act against their will. Kanter (1985) makes this point forcefully when he states that '. . . our client's wishes deserve our respect but not always our support . . . if we pretend that such interventions are collaborative we may further invalidate the perceptions of persons who are already confused about their social reality' (p. 84). Such candour may also have therapeutic value. It may give some people a sense of containment to be told that if the case manager is convinced they will harm themselves, then they will be forced to consider arranging an assessment for compulsory admission. An important caveat here is the potential for abuse of this power. Many workers and users will be familiar with situations where a user has been coerced into a course of action by the threat of compulsory admission.

For most users it may be unnecessary to confront them at an early stage with the possibility that the case manager may have to act against their will, as there is little reason to predict that this will actually take place. However, where there is a possibility of the case manager having to adopt a non-collaborative approach, the earlier that this can be shared with the user then the more opportunity there is for the user and case manager to discuss the implications and feelings that it provokes. Being open with the user may make it easier in the long run to maintain a relationship with them after an episode when the case manager has had to take control of aspects of their life.

One of the most difficult aspects of case management arises from the necessity to develop a close relationship with a needy person. The case manager must be clear, both for themselves and the user, about the personal boundaries around their relationship. Many case management services have an egalitarian ethos, and case managers dress informally and encourage users to address them on first name terms (Kanter, 1985). However, unlike some other professionals (such as lawyers or accountants), case managers do not invite their clients to partake in their social lives and encourage them to become personal friends. In case management, as in other caring roles, confusion over personal boundaries can too easily become abusive. If users are feeling vulnerable and insecure, ambiguity about the relationship can handicap them further, particularly if they have problems in interpreting and validating the outside world.

Leave users with as much power as possible

Often, users are not used to choice. They have been channelled and marginalized for so much of their lives that they may often make few demands and let the case manager pursue objectives that they quietly find of little relevance to their own experience and expectations. Case managers should be assertive in asking users for their opinions on what is happening.

Leaving power with the user means giving them choice. As

far as is practically possible, the case manager should arrange to see the user where and when the user prefers, rather than fitting the user into some predetermined schedule. Case managers also need to be flexible about the duration of any single contact that a user can tolerate. For some users, an hour of talking may be perceived as highly pressurizing. It is important to allow the user to set the pace and pattern of the work done.

Give permission for the user to rely on you

Case managers are in the business of offering support over periods when the user may experience varying levels of ability to cope. While promoting independence, the case manager also needs to give permission for the user to rely on them during times when they may be more dependent. This involves teaching users about normal, necessary and constructive dependence as might be experienced during a crisis. In practice, however, this trust is often only developed through the user having cause to rely on the case manager. It is obviously crucial that they are not let down.

Communicate effectively

One of the most lamentable aspects of professional training in mental health is its tendency to teach students jargon without teaching them how to prevent it becoming an impediment. Jargon can be a useful shorthand in some very tightly prescribed situations but more often it serves to mystify work in the field of mental health and creates a barrier between service providers and users. It seems that the most highly trained workers run the greatest risk of baffling people. Workers should constantly monitor their language and ask themselves whether it can be realistically decoded. Useful safeguards include establishing a working atmosphere where the user is encouraged to check any ambiguities with the case manager, and asking co-workers, both during joint clinical work and at clinical review meetings, to pick up on the use of jargon.

In trying to communicate complex issues, it can be helpful to introduce illustrative examples from the case manager's own experience. The use of diagrams and flow-charts can also be useful when describing circularity and feedback. It also presents the user with something concrete and tangible to take issue with. Effective communication can also be promoted by attempting to use the language, communication styles and metaphors used by the user. However, this is a highly developed skill and if the case manager's natural style deviates too far from the user's, they risk appearing false. The overriding necessity is that case managers should feel comfortable in their communication style while remaining intelligible.

ASSESSMENT

Information gained through assessment should drive case management and service development. Assessment is the task on which all else depends.

Procedures for assessment should be valid (a true picture of the user's situation), reliable (so that the results would be similar whoever did the assessment) and efficient (e.g. avoiding duplication with other services) (Welsh Office Social Services Inspectorate, 1990). The following describes how this can be achieved through:

1. an assessment process that maximizes the user's opportunity to voice their own concerns;
2. the clear specification of the content of assessment; and
3. close liaison with others involved (including other workers and carers).

Key features of assessment

Users identify their own needs wherever possible

The object of assessment is to gain a developing picture of the needs and strengths of the user and their social and physical environment. However, definition of need presents a difficult issue. A need can be considered as a problem or deficit, a desire, a demand, or a solution (Huxley 1990). Services tend to define need in terms of the services available. Thus assessment becomes an exercise in establishing the user's eligibility for services. Clearly assessment of this kind provides no inform-ation on needs that are not already addressed by existing services, and so does not inform service development. This presents a dilemma. It is very difficult for people to construct a picture of their needs without knowing what is on offer. The problems that users personally define as needs, and those they present as demands, are influenced both by their expectations of the resources available through case management and their expectations of their quality of life. Case managers therefore have the difficult task of exploring the user's situation with them without taking an overly narrow view of need or raising unrealistic expectations.

It is important that users tell case managers about their situation rather than have case managers rushing forward with direct questions about their mental state or a pithy but premature formulation. Users should be encouraged to de-scribe their everyday difficulties in their own words and at their own pace. It is important not to sacrifice rapport for the sake of information-gathering. The user needs to decide themselves what and when to disclose, and the case manager will gain nothing by conducting a structured interrogation.

Open questioning helps to avoid setting the user's agenda for them. These are questions that do not have a 'yes' or 'no' answer. For example, 'What do you feel are your main difficulties?' or 'What would you need to achieve in order to feel that you were improving?' are open questions that demand a description from the user, whereas 'Do you have problems going out?' or 'Do you sometimes feel the television is talking about you?' do not invite an expansive response. When the user has exhausted their account of their present situation the case manager can then use prompts in order to explore specific areas not already covered. This should continue to employ open questioning (e.g. 'What does your family make of this?' rather than 'Do you have any family problems?').

It can be helpful to reflect back some of the points the user is making in order to indicate listening and understanding, and to achieve further clarity. Interpretations, particularly of a psychodynamic nature, should be avoided unless they are presented tentatively as a way of clarifying the situation, and the user is invited to reject them. Interpretations may disempower people by undermining their own understanding of their situation, and risk imposing the worker's own model (based upon their own values) of what is going on.

A need may not become a demand if the user feels able to cope using their own resources. Although this should be respected, the case manager should not withhold information on help that is available. Alternatively, the case manager may identify a need which is not presented as a demand by the user. The case manager should share their views with the user, unless this would be severely detrimental to their relationship or would cause the user to cease contact. For example, the case manager may identify a need for the user to cease some form of abusive behaviour within their family.

Assessment should take place in an environment in which the user can relax

The positive effects of seeing users in their usual environments have been discussed earlier. The user's home is usually the place where they are most able to relax and involve other concerned people. However, there are exceptions. The user may be in an abusive relationship and can only speak freely away from the family home. They may consider a home assessment an invasion of privacy and request to be seen elsewhere. Sometimes the user's living conditions are so meagre that it is physically very awkward to perform the assessment. For example, assessments involving more than two people in a bed-and-breakfast room can feel like having a conversation with a bus queue. The case manager should be flexible and imaginative about where to perform the sessions, and should be guided by the preferences of the user. Sufficient privacy is a minimum condition.

There are dangers to the case manager in assessing in the home environment. They are not so able to manage the interaction with the user and have to deal with the user's unexpected visitors, phone calls, television, over-friendly (or otherwise) pets and unremitting offers of refreshment. On the other hand, this itself can offer valuable insights into the user's life. If, as a case manager, you are having trouble thinking straight, imagine how it must be for the user. A good starting point for collaborative problem-solving is to work with the user on how they can make the sessions more productive (e.g. by turning off the TV and putting the cat out).

The case manager may also be at risk of physical violence when visiting homes. There is a danger of overstating this risk. Often, users have a whole mythology surrounding them which affects the way in which services respond to them. This may make them *feel* dangerous, and thus contributes to a vicious circle. Imagine yourself trying to communicate with two anxious young workers who are more concerned about the location of the door and their personal alarms than what you are saying. However, such consideration should not lead the case manager to take risks. It will be much easier for a positive relationship to develop if everyone involved is able to relax. One approach is to work collaboratively with users at an early stage on the problem of their being, or appearing to be, dangerous.

The risk of abuse goes both ways. The user is at heightened risk of abuse by the case manager if seen in the isolation of their own home. Sexual and physical abuse of users by therapists, although little documented, is certainly a reality in some shameful cases (Masson, 1988). Joint interviews with other colleagues and involving other members of the user's social network in assessment means that everybody is chaperoned.

Attention to difference should be maintained

An important aspect of the social environment that must not be neglected is the case manager themselves. As with engagement, it will be easier for the case manager and user to communicate effectively if they are able to share common experiences and backgrounds.

Assessment should involve people close to the user

It is usually helpful to involve others close to the user in achieving an initial assessment although the method will vary from user to user according to their wishes. Some may prefer to be surrounded by family and friends. Others may wish to see you alone first so that they can tell their story without fear of contradiction. These wishes should be respected. However, the case manager should be alert to the user preventing other people from contributing to the assessment. If this occurs, the case manager can only raise this with the user. They do not have a mandate to approach the other parties without their consent. When the arrangements for the assessment are made by other members of the user's social network and the user is having trouble finding a voice among them, the case manager may need to assertively request time alone with the user.

Occasionally, when assessing the user among their family, it becomes apparent that the referred person is not the one most in need of services. Other family members may be displaying more distress or disorder, or be playing a more pivotal role in maintaining the family in a dysfunctional pattern of inter-action. In these situations the case manager can suggest family work. This could involve joint work with another worker, or another team member working to engage the other family member afresh.

Case managers are not qualified to assess every area of need

It is not the job of case managers to actually perform a com-prehensive assessment of need. It is their job to ensure that the assessment gets done and compile the information into a coherent, communicable whole.

> Mr W was referred to the EIS by a local field social worker, as his neighbours had been complaining of his bizarre behaviour, and the smell emanating from his flat. He was allocated for assessment to Jean, the team's occupational therapist, who visited Mr W at home with the social worker. Both Mr W and his apartment were in chaos and covered in faeces. He was communicative but extremely deluded and clearly unable to maintain himself. He had infected sores on his legs and was suffering the effects of uncontrolled diabetes.
>
> Jean took her initial assessment back to the team and assumed case managing responsibility. Jean's skills as an occupational therapist were clearly relevant to Mr W's case

as his level of self-care was minimal. However, there was also much more needed by way of assessment, and Jean asked the team's psychiatrist to evaluate Mr W's mental state. Jean also needed to sort out Mr W's housing status, and for this she drew on the expertise of others in the team, particularly the social workers.

Through repeatedly meeting with Mr W, she was able to establish considerable rapport and gained a clearer view of his needs and preferences. He clearly wished to remain in his own home. However, his general medical problems needed to be sorted out and so he agreed to go into hospital for treatment of his legs and his diabetes. During this time the 'hit squad' of local authority cleaners came to make his apartment habitable once again.

On Mr W's return, weekly home help and district nurse visits were arranged. These regular visitors to the flat were aware of the need to contact Jean should Mr W encounter further problems and Jean herself visited on a regular basis.

Jean's job as case manager for Mr W was to make sure all his needs were adequately assessed by experts and that he received the help he needed. It would have been unrealistic for Jean to have undertaken the whole task of assessment and service provision herself.

Assessment does not stop

Users and their environments are in constant dynamic change. Often it is only through making things happen that important aspects of the user's relationship with their environment become apparent. For this reason, assessment can never be said to be complete. It must be continually developed and refined. The information collected through assessment can be sought over protracted periods and from sources other than the user.

The content of assessment

There is no minimum amount of data on which the case manager can begin to plan. Often simply recognizing that someone is distressed is enough signal that something must be done. Nonetheless, when it comes to planning, the more information the better.

The Welsh Office Social Services Inspectorate (1990) recommended that case management assessment should sample:

1. self-care, activities of daily living and risk;
2. physical health;
3. mental health;
4. abilities and lifestyle;
5. the contribution of carers;
6. social network and support;
7. housing and finance;

with the amount of detail sought varying with the presentation of the user.

Focusing specifically on people with severe and long-term problems, Sherman (1989) described a comprehensive record-keeping system that emphasizes the kinds of clinical and administrative decisions needed for proactive case management. Information collection starts at the point of referral and includes user demographics, aliases, legal status, last known medication regime, dangerousness to self and others, known criminal acts, previous mental health treatment, diagnosis, presenting symptoms and problems, recommendations on how to stabilize the user in crisis, substance abuse behaviours, referral source, justification for nomination for assessment, hints on how to locate the user, and which staff know the user best. During initial face-to-face contacts further demographic and historical information is collected including the duration since first diagnosis, marital history, their type of residence, who the user resides with, employment status, household income, number of dependants, and highest educational level attained. The Denver Citywide programme also uses a problem checklist (Ellis, Wilson and Foster, 1984) which broadly covers nine dimensions: socio-legal status, substance abuse, medical/physical illness/injury, thinking disorders, personal distress, personal behaviour, interpersonal relations, role performance and ability to meet basic needs.

The EIS employed a similar format (based on records devised by Fagin and Purser, 1986, and others) incorporating a registration form containing information to be used in planning an assessment, and an assessment form which includes further information to be collected over subsequent contacts. The registration form included the nature of response requested (i.e. assessment only, direct clinical intervention or advice or consultation), the response time requested, significant other people involved (e.g. family), other involved workers that could join in the assessment, the user's first language, their country of birth, religion and ethnic origin, their doctor and their domestic situation.

The assessment form was designed to reflect the process of a typical first encounter and so starts with the history of circumstances leading to assessment, the user's attitude towards contact with the service, personal history, family history and the nature of present family relationships, and the user's main difficulties as they presently perceive them. For research purposes diagnoses were made according to ICD10 diagnostic criteria (World Health Organization, 1988).

There is no definitive statement of the information that needs to be assessed by case managers, and new packages are constantly coming to the fore (e.g. 'Homepack' from the Community Psychiatric Research Unit; Baldwin et al., 1991; Careplan; and from Research and Development for Psychiatry, London). Importantly, records should complement rather than impair good practice in assessment and planning. For example, there is a risk that checklists become used as a series of closed questions to the user rather than as an aide memoire.

Joint working

When assessing jointly with another worker, it is important to allow some preparation time so that each has access to the same information and tasks are sensibly allocated. For example, it is usually helpful if one worker leads the assessment so that the user can focus on one person at a time. Sometimes it is necessary for each assessor to inquire about particular topic areas according to their expertise. In family interviews it can also be helpful if assessors focus on the perspectives of different family members. Situations where the assessors are falling over each other to pursue the same line of inquiry should be avoided.

A framework for a dynamic picture

The case manager will soon collect a lot of information about the user and their environment. The next challenge is to use this information constructively. This requires a coherent framework.

One problem with the medical model described earlier is that it freezes time by taking a snapshot of needs that the user is presenting and then sticks a label on it. Functional analysis is a framework for considering assessment in a more dynamic manner (Owens and Ashcroft, 1982). It is a strategy for problem-solving rather than a psychological theory and so offers a common language for workers from different theoretical persuasions. Although designed for clinical problems, it was found useful at the EIS for mapping out a wide range of presenting problems and their contexts.

The model looks for circularity in the way people function and focuses on these feedback loops as targets for intervention. Functional analysis requires a clear specification of the presenting problems and a classification of the various events and variables that surround them according to (a) whether they serve to increase or decrease the probability of a problem, and (b) whether they occur before or after a problem.

A functional analysis takes a similar approach to behavioural analysis in which events are classified in an ABC configuration, where B refers to the behaviour in question, A to its antecedents (e.g. what happens before, where it happens, who with), and C to the consequences (e.g. what happens as a result, how people respond). For example, the problem behaviour may be a child's severe tantrums (B) that reliably occur when passing the sweet counter at the supermarket check-out (A) and that are immediately followed by the purchase of sweets (C) in order to minimize parental embarrassment. It is reasonable to hypothesize that the sweets may be serving to strengthen the likelihood and severity of tantrums at the check-out. The difference between a functional and a behavioural analysis is that the variables of a functional analysis need not be specified in behavioural terms, and the ABC analysis is applied repeatedly in order to discover the circularity that is maintaining the situation in its present state.

The development of a formulation using this approach is

like an experiment undertaken by the user and case manager as collaborators. On the basis of a crudely sketched out picture, their working hypotheses, they can attempt to change the presenting problems by manipulating either the environment that precedes the problem or by attempting to change its consequences. The effect of this on the presenting problems informs the further development of the functional analysis and future intervention. This systematic approach to the way people think, act and feel helps establish a developing picture of what is happening. The resulting functional analysis and the interventions that follow from it are complex and unique to the user.

The following case example is shown diagrammatically in Figure 6.2.

Mr B was a forty-year-old Welshman diagnosed as a dangerous paranoid schizophrenic. He was first diagnosed after a severe breakdown early in his working life as a printer and had been receiving medication for many years. During the 18 months prior to referral to the EIS he had deteriorated significantly with frequent admissions following claims that he was going to kill someone. His behaviour on the ward was seen by nursing staff as somewhat phoney, but his consultant psychiatrist felt he had a severe major mental disorder warranting (unsuccessful) referral to a secure unit. Mr B's behaviour included holding staff gently by the neck while displaying a Bela Lugosi leer, tangential speech, reporting ideas of reference (e.g. interpreting advertising hoardings as references to himself), and apparent attempts at suicide through plugging himself into the electricity supply. Nonetheless, he appeared to be an essentially gentle and whimsical person and he was popular among patients and nursing staff.

Mr B was seen at home with his wife by two EIS workers. They were struck by the strangely theatrical quality of his craziness and the way in which this was dealt with. Mr B's main reported problem was a fear that he was going to go crazy and murder Mrs B or himself. This fear was at its greatest (according to diary records that he was asked to keep) when Mr B was wrestling with negative thoughts or feelings, particularly concerning his wife. When Mr B expressed his feelings of dangerousness to his wife she would understandably become fearful and give all their kitchen knives to their neighbours. This seemed to have the effect of making Mr B feel even more dangerous.

The theatrical quality described earlier extended to their continued and effusive expressions of love for each other and their firmly held belief that everyone else should also offer unconditional love to each other. In addition Mr B used various cognitive strategies, such as mentally counting or repeating phrases to avoid negative thoughts, effectively inhibited the expression of unpleasant thoughts or feelings. The ongoing stress that this situation created led Mrs B to drink heavily. If Mr B was able to show the merest glimmering of negative feelings his wife responded with highly intellectualized interpretations, drawing on her reading of books on popular psychology, spiritualism or the occult.

The local accident and emergency department responded to Mr B's expressed dangerousness by regularly admitting him to the refuge of the hospital ward. Admissions seemed to be part of an addictive cycle in that they provided huge amounts of re-assurance and containment, thereby rewarding his mad behaviour. However, hospital admission also served to increase his concern over dangerousness since hospitalization, diagnosis and the way his consultant interacted with him confirmed his self-perception as a potentially violent, mad person. As this cycle perpetuated, Mr and Mrs B became more socially isolated and withdrawn. This included avoidance of any media for fear of encountering disturbing material. Both complained of marital tension manifest in a poor sexual relationship. For Mr B this seemed quite central and contributed to negative feelings about his wife.

Looking into Mr B's past seemed to offer clues regarding more distant antecedents to his concern over negative feelings. His parents had died when he was a toddler and his elder sister had been killed in tragic circumstances during his early teens. Their loss had seemed to be a pre-occupation of his over the years and had never been resolved. He had been brought up by his grandmother, a frail and critical lady whose house was 'like a museum'. The young Mr B could never be noisy or boisterous, and was frequently blamed for any distress experienced by his grandmother.

Mr B was encouraged to express his negative feelings in an acceptable way by keeping a record of them for discussion when the EIS workers visited. Mr and Mrs B also received communication skills and problem-solving training (in the manner described in Falloon *et al.*, 1984) focusing on the expression of negative feelings in a clear and unemotional way that allowed the other party to rectify any annoying behaviour. Mrs B was encouraged to help her husband express negative feelings by not intervening with interpretations and was helped to establish a link with a local counsellor who was able to assist her with her alcohol abuse. Mr B began attending a local day centre with a view to attending a work project.

Over several months Mr and Mrs B had established a new routine in which they were together less but spent that time more harmoniously. Mr B reported far less concern over his potential to harm and had not sought re-admission, aside from during one crisis when the EIS faciliated an early discharge.

In no sense could Figure 6.2 be described as a statement of the psychological truth of Mr and Mrs B's circumstances. It merely provided a way of looking at their situation in all its complexity and in a way that could be easily communicated to them. It was useful to literally build the picture with them, incorporating or removing links over time. Sketching out the functional relationships in this way helped illustrate where and how solutions could be attempted.

Use of formal assessment procedures

There is a range of assessment instruments or technologies that the case manager can draw upon. Each has its unique range and limitations of application but in general they are worth considering as they offer a way of establishing a baseline against which change can be evaluated.

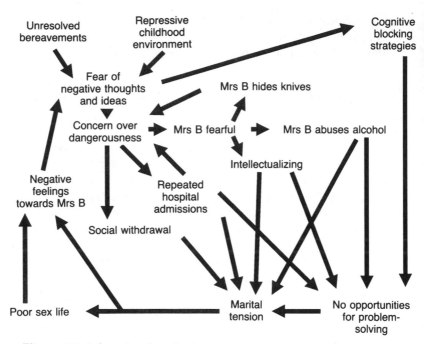

Figure 6.2 A functional analysis.

Self-report measures in the form of questionnaires are easy to administer and usually easy to score. Popular examples include the Fear Survey Schedule (Geer, 1965), the Speilberger State Trait Anxiety Inventory (Speilberger, Gorsuch and Lushene, 1970) and the Beck Depression Inventory (Beck *et al.*, 1961). Their disadvantages are that they:

1. are influenced by the motivation of the user and unconscious cuing by the assessor (Hersen and Bellack, 1976);
2. offer only one measure which may not correlate with changes in the user's physiological state or behaviours over time (Rachman and Hodgson, 1974);
3. have been developed primarily for users with problems related to depression or anxiety, and as such are not suited to those who are very distressed or disturbed or to people with poor reading skills;
4. often rely for interpretation of scores on norms derived from populations that may have little relation to the user.

Self-monitoring may have more to recommend it. Here the user simply records some specified event through diary records or the use of event counters. For non-observable events, such as auditory hallucinations or obsessive ruminations, self-monitoring is the only option available. It is also necessary where intrusion is impractical or impossible, for example in monitoring sexual behaviour. Problems with self-monitoring include the need for high motivation on the part of the user, unreliability and the fact that the act of keeping a record may itself affect the frequency of the event in question.

Direct observation offers a more accurate way of measuring change. There is a range of ways to structure the direct observation of users. The most basic is to look at the products of behaviour such as changed body weight or cigarette butts. Here the behaviour is not directly observed but inferred from its products and as such, it runs the risk of being falsified (e.g. using diuretics rather than dieting to achieve weight loss). Other methods involve recording behaviour as it occurs ('event recording'), or recording its duration ('duration recording'), or its occurrence over a certain time period ('time sampling'). Event recording is good for discrete and easily identifiable behaviours (such as verbal interaction with another person), while duration recording is suitable for longer behaviours (such as sleeping). Time sampling involves recording the occurrence or non-occurrence of behaviours during predetermined time samples. Clearly, these techniques make considerable demands on the time and motivation of observers and are rarely used outside institutional settings (see Hersen and Bellack (1976) for more details).

Probably the most widely used method of formal assessment is behavioural rating scales. A popular example is the REHAB package which involves a keyworker rating the user on an array of continuums according to their recollection of the user's behaviour over the past week. The scores can be summed and compared against norms for various populations in order to determine the most appropriate environment for rehabilitation. The authors present good reliability and validity data (Baker and Hall, 1983).

However, behavioural rating scales also have very limited application outside institutional settings. In addition they can

form the basis of service planning while neglecting the preferences of service users and grouping them together on
the basis of some specified definition of dependence. The
continuums represent a limited view of the range of important
behaviours that the user exhibits.

In conclusion, although formal assessments may be a useful
adjunct to an overall assessment of need in certain situations,
their application is inescapably limited. Arguably they present
a version of the medical model for application to psychosocial
problems by offering a diagnosis of disability based upon
statistically derived norms. The glamour of apparently scientific technologies should not be allowed to detract from what
users tell you they need. The overall message for formal
assessments is 'handle with care'.

INDIVIDUAL SERVICE PLANNING

The product of assessment is the individual service plan. The
function of the plan is to record the needs and strengths of the
user and the steps to be taken to improve their situation. It is
an ongoing dynamic record that changes with the ongoing
assessment of the user's needs and the continuous monitoring
of outcomes.

The process of individual service planning used at the
EIS had two stages running in parallel and was recorded
on different forms.

The needs/strengths record

This record simply consisted of two columns headed 'needs'
and 'strengths'. The simplicity of the form reflected the need
to take a graduated approach to planning. Users presenting
in crises were usually not ready to begin setting goals for
themselves and were more concerned with containing the
situation in the best way possible. During this period they
were more dependent on the case manager to take the lead
than subsequently, and so it was not a good point to begin to
making firm plans.

At the top of the 'needs' column were sample questions

such as 'What are your major difficulties?', 'Why do you feel you have difficulty dealing with . . . ?'. The 'strengths' column was headed by questions such as 'What do you feel you do best?', 'What are your best qualities?', 'Who do you find most easy to talk to?', 'What things do you (or did you until recently) enjoy?', 'How do you relax?'. As with assessment of needs, the aim in assessing strengths is to draw out those particular attributes, skills, knowledge and experience inherent to the user along with consideration of the resources in their environment and the positive ways in which they interact with them.

The user's needs and strengths are jotted down with the date of each entry. At this stage they are expressed in a general way. In terms of focusing on need, it is better to write 'to be more active' than 'to attend the art group at the day hospital three times a week'. The latter is not a need but a solution (and probably not a very good one). A 'need' can refer to ambiguous therapeutic goals ('to explore my feelings about my childhood') or quite specific practicalities (e.g. 'to get some clothes', 'to find somewhere to live'). A 'strength' includes anything that the user enjoys, likes about themselves or is good at (e.g. 'playing cards', 'getting on with my probation officer'). The most important requirement is that what is written on the form corresponds with what the user is trying to convey, and this should be checked with them.

The outcome/approaches record

The needs and strengths are then translated into specific outcomes sought and approaches to those outcomes. These again are checked out with the user and are written in such a way that anyone picking up the form would be able to understand it. Outcomes must be clearly specified and include an observable result. For example, 'To be more outgoing' is not enough. 'To speak to one new person this week' is a lot clearer. 'To have moved flat in the next year' is concrete enough and can be specified in terms of an approach such as 'To contact the housing department to find out about flat exchanges'. Sometimes desired outcomes are about further assessment, for example, 'To assess hearing' or 'Find out what

I'm good at'. Corresponding approaches to achieving these would be 'To arrange an out-patient appointment at the audiology department' or 'To attend a training centre for a two-week work skills assessment'.

In specifying approaches it is important that users are involved in determining the best approach. Often they will have attempted many solutions already and this experience should inform any future planning. Exercising choice demands information about the relative costs and benefits of each alternative approach in both personal and financial terms. Interim outcomes can usefully include trials of different alternatives.

The form should include details of where and when the approach is to take place and who is to be involved. Respective responsibilities and an estimated time scale for achievement of the aim should be spelled out. In some cases the outcomes/approaches record can be used as a form of contract between the case manager, the user and others involved with the work. The outcome/approaches record collects information for regular reviews of progress and is discussed later under 'monitoring'.

The above examples are worded from the point of view of users. The case manager will also have their own desired outcomes and approaches that should be recorded and reviewed in the same fashion. For example, returning to the case of Mr X, there was a need to provide continuing assessment and support during his stay in hospital following amputation of part of his foot. The objectives of this work were to:

1. determine the extent to which his craziness and paranoia related to his poor physical condition, his marginal social situation and his addiction to minor tranquillizers;
2. discover whether he could achieve sufficient insight to adjust to the amputation;
3. ascertain if he could find the motivation to care for himself and, depending on the results of these inquiries;
4. to determine and arrange the sort of support and accommodation that would suit him best at discharge.

At this stage a process of relationship building, assessment and planning has been set in motion. We now turn to a range of activities aimed at improving the user's quality of life.

Chapter 7

Tasks of case management II – environmental interventions

LINKING

Linking is the task of working with users to develop their network of support. The aim is to gather resources together in order to improve outcomes for users. Where it involves the case manager buying in services, I have defined it as brokerage and consider it separately below.

Linking is the case management task that most closely resembles advocacy. It involves petitioning other agencies for support and input, and it may mean arguing for extra resources in order to provide needed input. More generally, linking involves encouraging and supporting users in making a physical connection with some form of supportive agency. This includes agencies concerned with material support such as welfare benefits and housing. Wherever possible, it should also include resources used by the general public rather than specialist mental health agencies. Often, linking involves helping users overcome bureaucracy. Indeed, this has been described as the very *raison d'être* of case management (Lamb 1980).

Linking often takes place within a system of overstretched providers with limited resources who may not welcome the further demands of a case manager as they battle for resources on behalf of users. The following are some guidelines for linking that aim to achieve the best outcomes for users in such an environment.

Guidelines for linking

Keep the aims of linkage in sight

The user's connection with another resource is not an end in itself. It has to serve a purpose for the user. Sometimes case managers and users learn a lot while trying to make a connection. At the eleventh hour users may feel that the resource is not really what they want and they wish to fulfil the need in a different way. The difficulty that the user has in getting to a resource may mean that they are not ready to take on the demands that it presents, or that the case manager has to provide more practical support, for example through getting the user physically escorted to where they want to be.

Maximize user autonomy

Sometimes case managers find themselves wanting the user to connect with a resource so much they almost pick them up and place them there. This is rarely appropriate and only serves to infantilize the user. Part of the art of linkage is to get the user to take maximum responsibility at every stage in the process of selecting where to go, getting there and staying there.

Establish contacts

As an expert environmental manipulator, the case manager must devote considerable time and energy to discovering and mapping out the environment. For new case managers this should form a major thrust of any induction programme. The case manager should make appointments to see key players in the locality in order to discuss how they may liaise with them. Kanter (1985) argues that successful collaboration relies on knowledge rather than the mechanics of purchase of services. It is important to establish the responsibilities of other agencies as it will be a considerable irritant for them to receive inappropriate requests. What do they feel are their particular strong points? Who are they most able to help? Are they bound to specific exclusion criteria? How do they measure success and what achievements can they report?

The case manager must be able to assure the receiving agency that the referral is appropriate, and remain available in case problems occur. Case managers need to be aware of the expectations of other services so that they can help the user and the service understand each other. Such knowledge also avoids overlapping input when coordinating a range of providers.

Often the agency will not only be a useful resource for users, but will also be an appropriate source of referrals. In addition, they will have their own pool of knowledge and experience to tap into. It is amazing how the process of mapping out 'healthy' parts of the system becomes self-generating and a rich network of valuable resources is unearthed. Key people to link in with include housing agencies, work projects, churches, local authority day centres, and community leaders. Lamb (1980) specifically recommends frequent meetings with representatives from social security offices. 'Often one finds at these meetings harassed dissatisfied workers who are as frustrated as the care givers with the inefficiency and red tape of their agencies. Further they may reveal how to bypass the regulations; **in a bureaucracy, for each and every regulation there is a way, or ways, to get around it'** (*ibid.*, p. 764, my emphasis).

Establishing contacts is a demanding task and case managers need to exercise considerable skill, competence and reliability in order to gain the interest and respect of other agencies.

Be personal

Overcoming bureaucracy is also about making the process personal. When making contact with an agency it is important to identify named individuals who appear to be able to make things happen. The case manager should aim to establish first name terms with that individual so that when they next encounter each other on the phone both know exactly who they are dealing with.

When advocating for the user it is important to convey a holistic picture of a person with rights. The user is not 'a schizophrenic needing a home' but an individual with a particular and unique set of needs deriving from specific aspects of their circumstances. The case manager needs to describe these in detail and get the other party to describe what they, as individuals within their organization, can do about it.

While presenting the user in a favourable light it is important not to distort or exaggerate. This damages the credibility of the case manager and any trust that has been established between agencies.

Assume an intention to help

It is generally advantageous to assume that the other worker will attempt to assist the user if possible. Although this may not accord with experience, it is helpful in avoiding a combative stance and draws the other worker into a collaborative, problem-solving approach to overcoming obstacles. If the other worker describes constraints beyond their control, assume they are aligned with the user by asking them how they themselves would overcome the barriers.

Assertion not machismo!

One of the main competences required for linking is to overcome any fear of the telephone. The case manager needs to be able to identify the key personnel and then clearly state the desired outcome. When this is resisted, as it so often is, it may seem that a more aggressive role is needed. Where the other party is denying a resource to which the user has a clear right, this may be appropriate. However, as Lamb (1980) points out, 'Too often . . . the advocacy role becomes like a war – a licence to ventilate hostility' (p. 764). Aggression is unlikely to serve the interests of the user or the case management agency. There are points at which the case manager must acknowledge' that they lack the clout to overcome the particular obstacle that the other agency is presenting and that an alternative solution is needed.

Reinforce the link

We are all susceptible to having our behaviour shaped by other people. If the worker from the receiving agency achieves anything, then they should be showered with praise for their efforts. Not only does this increase the likelihood of them performing similar miracles in future, it may spur them on to even greater achievements. It also creates a positive working atmosphere and improves individual relationships.

Be creatively positive (and positively creative)

As previously described, the aim in linking is to fulfil a stated need, and there are always alternative methods. If one door shuts another may open. The user's experience and expectations may have shaped them into an expert at failure. The case manager must counterbalance their negative expectations by suggesting small ways in which the goal can be approached, thus giving the user a sense of achievement on which to build. While never deceiving the user or building up false expectations, the case manager can help to engender a sense of hope through setting realistic goals and problem-solving for creative solutions.

Part of operating creatively involves being able to move beyond both role and geographical boundaries in order to achieve desired outcomes. This may demand considerable support and guidance from other team members and line managers.

Use the team

No matter how much is learnt through experience of linking, case managers often find themselves confronted with paralysing gaps in their own knowledge. The user presents legitimate demands that have exhausted the creative resources of both user and case manager. This is a point at which the team offers an invaluable resource of expertise and experience. Often, other case managers have tackled the issue themselves or will be able to suggest ways of generating solutions. The team also provides a forum for finding out from others what they would expect from a particular course of action. In this way, the team becomes a testing ground for innovation.

Expect trial-and-error

With the user's constantly changing constellation of needs and strengths, it should be no surprise that linking is a trial-and-error process. Initial appointments are not attended, or after a short while the user gives up the form of support that has been actively striven for. This can be disheartening for all concerned unless a realistic perspective is maintained. It is almost inevitable that finding an appropriate network of support will require that the user samples options and rejects them, and it is important that the knowledge gained from each 'failure' is used to inform future attempts. The user may find they were not adequately prepared to exploit the opportunities that involvement with the receiving agency presented. They may find that the new situation demanded skills that they simply did not possess, or that they were inadequately supported to learn new ways of coping on-the-job. Often, change itself is simply too stressful, and the case manager and the user need to think creatively about ways of breaking down the task of becoming involved with the other agency such that a more graduated approach becomes possible.

It is easy for users to feel punished by the experiences of rejection and failure when trying to develop support networks. In almost every situation, there is some aspect of behaviour that is worthy of praise and these should not be neglected. For example, if the user turned up on the first session of evening classes but never attended again, the initial attendance should be marked out as a considerable achievement on which to build. An advantage of working collaboratively with users is that difficulties can be shared and perspectives on the episode pooled in order to inform future planning.

Kanter (1985) is one of the few authors to consider the psychological aspects of linking and the relationship between user and case manager. He usefully underlines the ambivalence that users are bound to feel over steps towards independence. He describes how young people with severe and long-term mental health problems are unable to reconcile the 'discrepancy between their fantasy of what they would like to be able to do and the reality of what they have done and are likely to do in the future . . . they either become immobilized in an overwhelming sense of emptiness and despair, or defend against such affects with grandiose ideation and troublesome social behaviour – often exacerbated by drug abuse – that impedes any further maturation' (p. 78). He also describes the problems they encounter accepting social roles and the fact that they generally fall back into a dependent or subordinate position which is detrimental to their sense of self-esteem.

Sadly, through adopting psychoanalytical explanations of failures in linking, Kanter places responsibility for problems in establishing networks firmly with the user. The reader interested in psychodynamic considerations is referred to his discussion of the user 'splitting' agencies and demonizing one while deifying another. Through such processes the user is seen as impeding communication between agencies and largely responsible for their own inertia. Other interpretations are possible. The user commenting on different agencies may reflect nothing more than their being a discerning consumer. If their messages are inconsistent then this is to be expected given their shifting perspectives and the conflicting anxieties they may feel about increased independence balanced against fear of failure or rejection by others. The problems inherent in a psychodynamic view are well illustrated by this quotation: 'More functional patients often have greater difficulty linking with community resources. In many instances, more chronic patients are more tolerant of the impersonal treatment that they receive with various social agencies. When individuals still have some hope of being treated decently, they find rules, regulations, and red tape more difficult to endure. With such persons, case managers should consult with staff in other agencies, orientating them towards the **narcissistic sensitivities** of such patients' (Kanter, 1985, p. 87, my emphasis).

Recognize limits of case manager advocacy

The above quote illustrates why users need independent advocates to argue on their behalf alongside case managers. They need to be assured of someone to whom they can turn with a grievance without fear of being labelled narcissistic. Case managers need to recognize the limits of their advocacy role imposed by their lack of independence from service systems. If no advocates are available and the case manager sees the user complaining about the way they are treated as a problem with **the user**, the user may find they have no one else to turn to for support.

An example of linking:

When it came to discharging Mr X following the amputation of part of his foot, it was found that no hostel would take him because of his history of aggression, disordered thinking and bizarre behaviour. The Homeless Persons Unit was very reluctant to place him in bed-and-breakfast accommodation because he was deemed intentionally homeless. The case manager overcame this through personal petitioning of people known to be receptive within the unit, arguing that there had been a change of circumstances both physically and socially. The District Nursing Service was also contacted to monitor his foot and to encourage compliance with medication. The case manager also arranged for Mr X to be registered with a family doctor.

Very soon, the nurses stopped visiting and the family doctor wrote him off his books because of reports of his previous aggression. Mr X interpreted this as rejection, became depressed and began to neglect his physical care. Fortunately, another more tolerant family practitioner was found who was able to develop a positive relationship with Mr X. In addition the District Nursing Service was persuaded to supply a male nurse to visit Mr X, at least for a follow-up period following discharge.

All attempts to link Mr X to any daytime activities were a failure at this stage. He was frequently drowsy and incoherent, apparently because of his chaotic use of minor tranquillizers. He would rage at the case manager for failing to obtain benefits that he believed himself to be entitled to. Eventually, he was found unconscious with an overdose and the case manager arranged an emergency admission with a view to reviewing his medication.

Due to pressure on beds he was prematurely discharged to a unit for homeless men, who in turn rapidly discharged him when they discovered his previous history and threatening behaviour. Meanwhile, because he had refused to make any payments for his bed-and-breakfast accommodation he was at risk of eviction. He was also becoming increasingly aggressive with the case manager who felt that co-working with another colleague was necessary to ensure adequate personal security.

A face-to-face meeting was arranged with the Homeless Persons Unit with the result that a very clear written contract was negotiated between Mr X and the housing department. To everybody's surprise Mr X fulfilled his side of the contract completely, making regular payments as specified. Following his overdose it became clear that withdrawal from minor tranquillizers was a priority and, after considerable trauma on all sides, this was eventually achieved through a structured reduction programme under the supervision of the EIS psychiatrist in liaison with his family practitioner. As a result his behaviour became less disinhibited, and he became more lucid, referring for the first time to his emotions. His interpersonal skills became more appropriate and he acknowledged some of the problems that faced him.

In reviewing the case, Mr X's case manager said, 'What has been most essential is the continuity of my contact throughout this period (one year), for on many occasions if we had lapsed contact it is very likely that he would have fallen through all the support networks and would probably have spiralled down to another cycle of self-neglect. The other main factor is that the problems were addressed on a multi-agency basis working directly with the district nurses, Homeless Persons Unit, in-patient psychiatry, out-patient psychiatry, the family practitioner and the medical unit. Similarly, it was only with good will and good communication between ourselves and the family practitioner that we were able to maintain the client on the benzodiazepine programme'.

BROKERAGE

Brokerage involves directly purchasing services on behalf of users and is considered here as a special form of linkage. It therefore encompasses the skills required for linking, along with additional safeguards to ensure good practice.

Brokerage involves presenting the user with a specific sum of money or a menu of resources that can be used in individual service planning. The following guidelines are intended to ensure that brokerage improves the quality of individual service planning.

1. Assessment is not restricted to those areas of need that the resource menu aims to satisfy.

2. The existence of services that can be bought directly does not prejudice the uptake of other resources that may be of more value to the user. Working with a limited range of services to buy directly runs the risk of blinkering case managers to other options. Some of these options may need to be resourced in a different way or may even be free to the general public. It is important that there are no implicit or explicit incentives for case managers to deploy specialized services rather than helping integrate users with communities through the use of ordinary facilities.
3. The user is kept fully and continuously up-to-date with the range of options that can be bought directly and their respective costs and benefits in both financial and personal terms.
4. Decisions on the total allocation of resources to users are not made by someone who is responsible for either identifying users for the service or assessing need. In order to promote service development that is influenced by unmet need, the identification and assessment of need should not be corrupted by consideration of resource implications. Otherwise there is an increased risk that assessment will only reflect the resources available, and that people who might place an increased strain on resources will not be identified.
5. All the requirements of continuous monitoring, feedback and independent advocacy continue to apply.

Brokerage should emphasize responsibility for decision-making on the part of case managers rather than merely their custodianship of resources (Welsh Office Social Services Inspectorate, 1990). This requires that financial and managerial responsibilities are aligned so that case managers are responsible not only for the financial consequences of their decisions, but also the achievement of those outcomes of importance to users.

A brokerage role sometimes involves case managers in determining eligibility for service provision. This is properly the responsibility of the service as a whole rather than individual workers and so is considered in Part Three.

WORKING WITH INFORMAL CARERS

The goal of working with informal carers is to involve them in an extension of the collaborative approach to problem-solving established with users. This should be routine practice rather than something that only occurs where carers are perceived as problematic (Smith and Birchwood, 1990). The same approach to engagement and relationship-building applies. In particular, the case manager should indicate respect for their position and an understanding of the situations they are having to address. Families are often wary of being blamed for their son or daughter's problems, and this should be countered by emphasizing the family's importance as a resource for care and support.

With their in-depth, long-term and frequent contact with users, families and partners are an invaluable resource in all the core tasks of case management (Intagliata *et al.*, 1988). Despite this they are often given inadequate information, and are rarely involved in individual service planning (Ryglewicz, 1984). Carers can also promote successful linkage and competence in activities of daily living through encouragement and practical assistance. Being independent of service providers, carers are particularly well qualified to monitor the outcomes of service provision and feed this information back to case managers or more formalized advocacy systems. They also have an important role in crisis intervention being ideally placed to spot early indications of impending problems. However, Intagliata *et al.* (1988) underline the importance of helping families set boundaries on their involvement to prevent stifling any opportunities for the user to learn from their own mistakes and glory in their own successes. Carers also need to be supported in seeking help should their involvement with the user become too burdensome.

While it is important for the case manager to involve and support carers, equally the case manager should not be drawn into supporting the family against the user. The case manager may need to work hard at presenting complaints as shared problems to be solved. An approach to family problem-solving is described later in this chapter.

The case manager must be clear with the family about what they as a worker can and cannot do, setting boundaries on involvement while leaving the family with as much control as possible. If the family situation is one of conflict, the case manager may need to underline that they are primarily serving the interests of the identified user while aiming to meet the needs of the family as a whole as a secondary consideration. For some families there may be little interest in the family functioning as a unit, and the concern is with ousting the user from home. Sometimes this is an appropriate mutual goal and, as with adolescence, if the user's concern is with separation then working with the family as a unit should not be seen as mandatory. Usually, however, family work is helpful, even to help family members part.

With the user's consent, merely exposing the family to the work that the case manager and the user are doing together can be helpful. It reduces the potential for fantasies about what may be happening and is particularly valuable if the family feel they are responsible for the user's problems and fear blame or rejection. Involving carers as far as possible maximizes support, and creates the opportunity for them to become involved in case management. In contrast, exclusion of the family may lead to misinformation and misunderstanding. The user may experience unnecessary stress through feeling caught between their case manager and their carers.

MAINTAINING AND EXPANDING SOCIAL NETWORKS

Poor social networks contribute to vulnerability to mental disorder (Brown and Harris, 1978) and are more often found among people receiving services than the general population (Lipton *et al.*, 1981; Brugha, 1984; Henderson, 1984). However, the relationship between social networks and mental health may be a complex one. Larger social networks are not necessarily beneficial (Cutler *et al.*, 1987) and much depends on the nature of relationships within the network; for example, whether relationships are reciprocal or one party is wholly dependent on the other, or whether the relationship is purely instrumental in achieving some end.

It is easier to maintain social networks than to rebuild them. Many of the services described in Chapter 3 worked with users who already have impoverished social networks; people who are single, live alone and have few social contacts. This provides a strong rationale for working with people in context and in a manner that complements their existing supports through the involvement of carers, joint assessment with other agencies already providing support and an emphasis on early intervention to prevent crisis causing unnecessary disruption.

There are many approaches to expanding social networks. The first objective is to help users exercise choice. For some, social contact may be aversive and a major stress factor in bringing about episodes of mental disorder. Withdrawal may be a valued coping skill in these cases. For others, motivation to engage in social activities may be very low. One major inhibitory factor is often anxiety. Entering social situations as a stranger uncertain of your abilities to cope requires considerable courage and this is easily neglected in goal setting. This is often associated with deficits in interpersonal skills and these are discussed below when looking at skills training.

There are, however, other strategies for expanding the social networks of users. For example, in the US the development of self-help groups as part of community support systems now has a strong pedigree and contributes greatly to social support, improved self-esteem and increased autonomy (Chamberlin *et al.*, 1989). Although the involvement of case managers in running or controlling self-help would be compromising and contradictory, they may have a role in allying themselves with the development of such initiatives and offering any resources and support that they have available. Survivors Speak Out and the Nottingham Patients Councils are two examples of successful British self-advocacy projects that have benefited from collaboration between mental health workers and users (Campbell, 1990).

Case managers may also have a role in inviting current users to assist each other. For example, one older user of the EIS who had been referred in a dangerously depressed state felt able after a while to escort a younger man back to work after a protracted period of withdrawal following an episode of severe craziness. The case manager here has a role as go-between, and is responsible for ensuring that both parties are not made to feel put upon. Minimal contracts underlining the right of either party to withdraw at any stage can be helpful and the involvement of a volunteer with a user should not incline a case manager to be less diligent in monitoring.

Users or ex-users can also be asked to undertake a more specifically therapeutic role. For example, Milne *et al.* (1989) trained ex-users as therapists in community groups for people suffering anxiety. Training raised the skills of ex-users in providing social support, was of benefit to group members and had no adverse effects on the users leading the groups.

More typically, a case manager will attempt to link the user to socially supportive agencies such as work projects, day care or community centres while simultaneously working with the user on their interpersonal skills. In some cases the case manager can usefully accompany the user in order to help them establish contact. In others it is clearly inappropriate. For the EIS this was particularly the case when trying to help isolated users establish contact with community centres concerned with particular minority groups (e.g. Portuguese or Afro-Caribbean centres). Strategies included liaising with workers or members at the centre to come out to the user or engaging the help of a volunteer of the same ethnic origin. These attempts at linking draw upon all the case manager's resources for seeking information on how best to proceed in a sensitive manner. Organizations such as the Afro-Caribbean Mental Health Association in London (Francis *et al.*, 1989) offer a resource for consultation to workers and operate their own advocacy and volunteer schemes. For example, they will help people reunite with estranged relatives following episodes of mental disorder and hospital admission. The case manager should be fully aware of the availability of such resources.

LIAISING WITH HOSPITALS

With effective case management the role of hospitals becomes more specialized. Stein and Test (1980) argued that, with adequate community programming, hospitals would only be used for users who are an imminent danger to themselves or others, people with mental disorders complicated by significant medical problems that require special diagnostic and treatment facilities, and for those 'whose psychosis is so severe that they require the structure and good nursing care that only a hospital can provide' (p. 397). However, on the latter point the authors were able to demonstrate positive outcomes for people described as acutely psychotic without hospitalization, and effective alternatives to hospitals are emerging (e.g. Parker and Knoll, 1990; Brunton and Hawthorne, 1989). Determining exactly for whom hospitalization is appropriate is a difficult decision to establish locally. It is influenced by the availability of tested alternatives, medical hegemony, and the prevailing values and beliefs about mental health service provision. However, most case managers working with people with severe and long-term mental health problems will need to consider their relationship with hospital-based workers.

The need for continuity of contact when users are admitted has already been underlined. Where informal relationships are ineffective, formal arrangements need to be instituted. The EIS case managers relied on negotiation with hospital-based consultants if a planned admission was sought. The success of this arrangement was totally dependent on the relationship established between the team and the consultant. In practice, the team's psychiatrist undertook the negotiation. Where it worked well this arrangement gave no cause for concern. However, with certain consultants the case manager was specifically barred from contact with the user during their stay in hospital. Such hit-and-miss arrangements do little to benefit the user.

Generally, the methods for establishing contact with psychiatrists are the same as for any other local service provider. However, for hospital-based consultants it can be helpful for the case manager to spend time attending ward rounds and offering case management for those 'most in need' at discharge. Such involvement with the hospital can serve to bridge the chasm between hospital and community care and provides an opportunity for the case manager to identify particular individuals to link up with when discontinuity of management threatens.

The establishment of effective working relationships with staff concerned with maintenance medication will be crucial to the success of plans for people who are known to benefit from psychotropic drugs. This is made much easier when the team has an in-house psychiatrist who is free to prescribe on the basis of their own assessment of the user's medical needs. However, this is often complicated by existing relationships between the user and hospital-based consultants. Whoever the case manager has to liaise with, it is worth their investing considerable effort in establishing a relationship of mutual respect and understanding.

The case manager has much to offer the fair-minded psychiatrist. Their continuous involvement allows the close monitoring of the effects of medication and the extent of the user's compliance with medication regimes. The case manager may also find themselves fulfilling a liaison role for users with regard to medication. This may take the form of advising the psychiatrist on the detrimental effects of the medication and requesting alternative medication or changes in dosage. The EIS was fortunate in that the level of communication between team members was such that the team's consultant psychiatrist was willing to prescribe on the basis of the assessment of other team members, although if further prescriptions were necessary the user was always seen by the consultant.

LIAISING WITH FAMILY DOCTORS

Family doctors are the hub of health care for their patients and for most people they are the most accessible and socially acceptable pathway to help. The family doctor is the best placed worker to identify early indications of impending crisis or relapse (Goldberg and Huxley, 1980). They are often known and trusted by users and have long-standing contact with both them and their carers. The EIS found that family doctors often value community-based working, joint working and easy referral (Onyett *et al.*, 1990) and were enthusiastic about offering accommodation for seeing users in the familiar and neutral environment of the doctor's surgery.

Liaising with family doctors may take the form of joint assessment and therapy, consultation, or simply high-quality communication. The EIS routinely informed family doctors of the outcome of assessments of their patients even if they were not the original referrers. This created an opportunity for them to comment on the service their patients were offered. This may be the only practical way of meeting the requirement that family doctors are involved with assessment as part of the care programme approach described in Chapter 2.

The EIS found that around a third of its users had significant physical problems (Onyett, 1992). This is far from atypical (Anthony and Blanch, 1989). The case manager may therefore need to assume an advocacy and monitoring role over general medical issues. This is often most effectively achieved via the medical and nursing members of the team. More specifically, as the family doctor remains primarily responsible for the medical welfare of the user, responsibility for prescribing psychotropic drugs can also remain with them. This means the psychiatrist literally acting as consultant to the family doctor, advising on the best approach to prescribing on the basis of a psychiatric assessment.

LIAISING WITH OTHER AGENCIES

The aim of this task is to maintain the availability and involvement of other agencies in order to promote choice and continuity of service provision for the user. Ongoing liaison promotes discussion of potential referrals, joint inter-agency assessment and the involvement of other workers in individual service planning. It is particularly important to sustain contact with agencies which are likely to maintain involvement subsequent to an episode of intensive case management.

Liaison with specific agencies can usefully be apportioned to different members of the case management team. It may be useful for ethnic minority workers who have particular knowledge and skills to liaise with community workers and agencies of the same ethnic background when attempting to maintain links with minority groups. For example, the EIS benefited from having a Malaysian community mental health nurse on the team who had an interest in liaising with agencies for Oriental single, homeless men. Other links may need to be established with key agencies such as hospital wards, hostels, health centres and social work departments.

The skills required for liaising with other agencies

encompass those needed for linking. In addition, the case manager may need to devote considerable time to regular visits to the agency concerned in order to become fully attuned to their culture and practice. This may be difficult to achieve in the face of pressing case load demands but can nonetheless be a worthwhile investment. This was particularly the case for the EIS's psychiatrist and occupational therapist when working with local hostels. They offered regular consultation sessions and were a named contact during crises.

The foregoing has been primarily concerned with manipulating aspects of the user's environment in order to promote positive outcomes. The next chapter takes a closer look at work with users within that context.

Chapter 8

Tasks of case management III – user and user-environmental interventions

This chapter combines those tasks concerned with the user themselves and those concerned with their interactions with their environment (Figure 6.1, p. 105).

TRAINING IN COPING SKILLS

Training in coping skills is usually considered part of the practice of psychiatric rehabilitation: 'the process of helping a physically or psychiatrically disabled person to make the best use of his residual abilities in order to function at an optimal level in as normal a social context as possible' (Bennett, 1978). All too often, however, rehabilitation is regarded as something which happens only during hospitalization or in the course of a structured day centre or day hospital-based aftercare programme. Deploying mobile and skilled case managers outside institutional environments allows users to work on developing skills in the situations in which they will need them.

Liberman *et al.* (1986) offer a conceptual framework for developing social skills training aimed at solving problems concerned with activities of daily living, medication management, money management, family relationships, job-finding, occupation, and friendship. The model places skills training within a stress-vulnerability framework and advocates rehabilitation through:

1. training the basic psychobiological and cognitive functions that form the internal representation of social situations (ensuring, of course, that the necessary prosthetics such as spectacles, hearing aids and dentures have been obtained);
2. training in receiving, processing and sending social

communications through behavioural rehearsal, coaching, reinforcement, modelling and homework, and;

3. working with the user's environment so that skills, however poorly developed, will be rewarded and supported by others.

Similar cognitive behavioural approaches have also been developed to alleviate hallucinations, delusions and 'negative' symptoms of major mental disorder such as apathy and social withdrawal (see Slade, 1990, and Tarrier, 1991, for reviews). Although the potential of these approaches is only just beginning to be explored, it is likely that they will be increasingly applied in the user's own social environments and will require skilled and mobile workers.

INDIVIDUAL TALKING THERAPY

The inclusion of individual therapy within the case management role requires qualification. The nature of the relationship between case manager and user has been described as a collaborative one in which imbalances of power are made explicit. This excludes from case management those forms of therapy that cannot be accommodated within such a relationship. That is those where the internal logic of the therapy is masked from the user and the motives behind interactions between therapist and user are not explicit.

Psychodynamic therapies (such as those based on the work of Freud and Jung) fall into this category. They run the risk of interpreting the user's experience in a way that can distort their perceived reality and leave them disempowered. Rowe (1988) summarizes the essence of dynamic psychotherapy thus: 'The psychotherapist is superior, the patient inferior. The psychotherapist, by virtue of his knowledge, training and special insight, has access to truths above and beyond the capacity of the patient. The psychotherapist's truths have a higher truth value than the patient's truths. The psychotherapist interprets the patient's truths and tells him what they really mean' (p. 13). Many mental health workers will have been involved in ward or day hospital-based 'community meetings' where staff have relentlessly interpreted the attempts of users to communicate. A familiar situation involves the user's complaints about the standard of food, reliably eliciting an interpretation about their not feeling adequately nourished in their relationships with key members of staff. This usually results in a glowing knowingness on the part of staff and frustration and anger on the part of the users who have to eat the lousy food. Gibson (1989) describes how poor staff communication and dangerous errors of decision-making follow from a tendency to act on the inferred meaning of what users are saying rather than what they are explicitly stating.

Reflective counselling and behavioural psychotherapy are useful for establishing a clearer understanding of the user's difficulties and helping them overcome anxiety-based problems. They may also be easier to incorporate within a collaborative relationship. However, in common with all therapies, they run the risk of imposing alien value systems on the user through the therapist's conviction that they know what is best for them, and victim-blaming by locating the need to change within the user's head. The uncritical application of cognitive therapy (where the object of therapy is to assist the user in making mood-improving attributions) is particularly prone to this latter fault.

Case managers need to be aware of the potential in therapy for harm (Masson, 1988) particularly since they are already in a powerful position with regard to users. The aim is that case managers should assume a therapeutic role, without necessarily doing therapy. This means endeavouring to offer the sort of relationship we would all seek: one in which we are listened to, taken seriously, respected and practically assisted.

DRUG THERAPY

As ever, enlightened psychiatrists are at the forefront of radical critiques of the myths and dogmas of their profession. For example, Liberman *et al.* (1986) criticized psychiatry's reliance on drug therapy since it fails to remedy the 'negative' symptoms of major mental disorder (such as apathy or withdrawal), has serious side effects giving rise to non-compliance, and does not teach users the skills they need for survival in the community. Other psychiatrists have concluded that the long-term prognosis for people diagnosed as schizophrenic has been unaffected by the introduction of the neuroleptics (Mosher and Burti, 1989; Warner, 1985). Mosher and Burti (1989) usefully distinguish the known effects of neuroleptic drugs from the 'mythical' unsubstantiated ones. The known effects are a reduction of the 'positive' symptoms of major mental disorder (such as hallucinations and delusions), shortened hospital stays, reduced re-admission rates, the production of tardive dyskinesia (involuntary movements of the lips, tongue, jaw and other parts of the body), a revitalized interest in schizophrenia and large corporate profits. Under 'mythical' effects they include the emptying of psychiatric hospitals, changes in the long-term social recovery rates of people diagnosed as schizophrenic, the enhanced learning of coping skills, an impact on the physiological aetiology of schizophrenia and the reduction of hospital admissions to almost zero if drug compliance is assured.

Mosher and Burti (1989) point out that while giving drugs is easy, psychosocial alternatives are far more complicated, expensive and difficult to implement. The best outcomes are often achieved through a combination of both (Tarrier, 1990). Nonetheless, it may be advantageous to avoid using drugs before psychosocial interventions have been tried, unless immediate alleviation of impenetrable craziness is necessary to avoid crisis, or the circumstances (e.g. a hotel room) do not contain the resources for effective psychosocial intervention.

If drugs are to be used, users should be fully informed of the therapeutic and side effects of the different options available, and if the user chooses to take drugs, Mosher and Burti suggest that they view it as an experiment. Users are not encouraged to hold any expectations about efficacy and are asked to monitor various aspects of their experience before and after taking the drugs (for example in terms of emotional state, bodily discomfort, and level of energy). Positive or negative changes are recorded on a daily basis and if any side effects emerge users are asked to get in contact with the service. The particular medication is then fine-turned or discontinued on the basis of their reports and those of carers or others involved.

Mosher and Burti advocate maintaining close enough contact with users to allow them to advise workers of impending feelings of craziness in order that action can be taken at the earliest opportunity. Importantly, the ultimate decision to take medication rests with the user.

Targeted drug treatment (Carpenter and Heinrichs, 1983) may offer an alternative to more traditional approaches to medication. This approach aims to treat symptoms as they arise rather than maintaining dosage when no symptoms are being reported. The reduced intake of drugs offers the potential to reduce serious side effects, such as tardive dyskinesia, and tailors medication more appropriately to the developmental stage of the user's difficulties. This is particularly important in view of the possibility that time itself may reduce the intensity of psychotic phenomena while increasing the risk of debilitating side effects. However, Carpenter *et al.* (1990) have shown that targeted medication may only be appropriate for selected users.

The fine-grain monitoring role described here is an appropriate case management task given their regular and frequent contact with both user and carers. Case managers would need to negotiate their role regarding the mechanics of medication management (such as giving injections and using pill counters or diaries) with the medically responsible worker and with regard to their own professional qualifications.

CRISIS INTERVENTION

Crisis intervention is one of the tasks primarily concerned with the interaction between the user and their immediate social environment (Figure 6.1, p. 105). Stress-vulnerability models underline the centrality of the management of crises for people experiencing episodic but severe distress over long periods.

Caplan's (1964) crisis theory assumed that individuals need to maintain a stable state in which they can anticipate new situations and determine their reactions to them. Crises occur when situations are perceived as being severely disruptive to the stability of individuals or the systems in which they live. The process of crisis can be broken down into four stages:

1. The individual is confronted by a problem that poses a threat to perceived needs and habitual problem-solving strategies are used in response.
2. If these familiar strategies fail, feelings of stress escalate and encourage trial-and-error attempts at problem-solving. These will normally be new to the individual and it is at this point that crises offer potential for new learning.
3. If the trial-and-error attempts are not successful, ineffective emergency measures may be attempted to alleviate the problem.
4. If these fail, stress increases to a level beyond the individual's capacity to cope and psychological dysfunction ensues to such a degree that the user may need to leave or be removed from the situation.

Clearly, the earlier in this process that the case manager can intervene, the better. Crisis prevention involves working with users to predict those situations which are most likely to create an intolerable threat to their equilibrium and then working through the consequences of various preventive strategies. A functional analytical framework can be useful in this form of problem-solving (Chapter 6). For example, where the crisis may arise because of fear of a specific situation, such as a return to work, the fear can be addressed through behavioural techniques such as anxiety management, role play and graded exposure.

Unfortunately crises do not always lend themselves to this sort of premeditated analysis. Very often the user finds themselves in the midst of crisis due to circumstances beyond their control. Here, the priority for the case manager is to get alongside the user and support them in problem-solving. This is a demanding task as crises often occur in a charged emotional atmosphere where the user appears to be unable to think or communicate clearly. However, as Hoult (1986) observed, 'It is surprising how often a solution appears for a seemingly intractable problem in a disturbed patient if one talks to him and his relatives for sufficient time' (p. 139). The art of crisis intervention is to remain involved and resist the urge to rescue the user when this may be ultimately unnecessary. The ideal outcome is for the user to find their own solution, often with the case manager managing the emotional atmosphere around them. Crisis management is largely about creating space for the user to problem-solve. Where this is not possible, because the user has become locked in an upward spiral of arousal and is unable to find solutions, the case manager needs to intervene directly, offering a strategy for reducing arousal to a level where the user can attempt to resolve the situation for themselves or allowing the user to become temporarily dependent on the case manager to sort out the crisis. Sometimes this involves the user having to be removed from the situation that is creating the crisis and it is at this point that the availability of residential alternatives to hospitalization are invaluable. Wherever the user is taken it is crucial that the case manager follows them. In this way both case manager and user are able to learn from the crisis and the opportunity is presented for developing collaborative relationships with staff in order to reduce the likelihood of inappropriate planning. Users also see that the case manager will maintain an involvement with them even when they are at their worst.

Crisis intervention does not end at this point. It is crucial that the user is returned to the crisis situation as soon as possible, equipped with new strategies and support for problem-solving. The case manager will need to commit considerable time to follow-up visits and contingency planning for future threats to equilibrium.

Crises are by their very nature unpredictable and emotive. For this reason it is important that case managers do not work alone. Joint working allows workers to help each other to remain as functioning problem-solvers in a crisis and increases their personal safety. It is also invaluable when it comes to workers 'debriefing' and winding down after a particularly arousing piece of work.

FAMILY THERAPY

Aside from supporting families and making appropriate use of the help that they are able to offer in performing case management tasks, it is often appropriate to consider working with the family as a whole in efforts to prevent or resolve crises.

There are many and varied approaches to family interventions (Ryglewicz, 1984). In common with individual therapy, some approaches run the risk of disempowering the user through regarding them as symptomatic of a wider family pathology or imposing values about the way in which family members (e.g. women) should behave (Williams and Watson, 1988). Family therapy is also unusually well endowed with jargon.

There is now a considerable body of research which points to the importance of patterns of family interaction in the outcome of major mental disorder. Families high in 'expressed emotion', a construct encompassing criticism, overinvolvement and poor problem-solving, are found to experience higher relapse rates among their diagnosed relatives. Reducing expressed emotion through education, relative groups and family work, or simply through reducing the amount of face-to-face contact within certain families has a positive effect on outcome (Leff *et al.*, 1982; Liberman *et al.*, 1984; Leff *et al.*, 1985). Although easily applied these approaches have had surprisingly little impact on practice (Mechanic, 1986).

Falloon *et al.* (1984) have described an approach to working with families that is effective and avoids the value-laden nature of much family therapy. Essentially it is a form of behavioural social skills training for families with the aim of improving their problem-solving skills. Therapy sessions take the form of workshops where the case manager has the task of coaching families in skills such as identifying positive things that other members are doing and communicating praise; expressing negative feelings in a clear way that allows the recipient to correct their behaviour; actively listening; making requests; and pinpointing and solving problems. Coaching takes the same form as any skills training: identifying areas to work on, modelling of the skill by the therapists, rehearsal, constructive feedback and reinforcement, and the use of homework assignments.

Although apparently quite simple, in practice behavioural family therapy was found at the EIS to have a powerful effect on the way family members regard each other and themselves. For example, the expression of positive feelings towards each other involves three steps: 'look at the person', 'say exactly what they did that pleased you', and 'tell them how it made you feel'. This may feel totally alien to many families and the task presents a considerable challenge. Yet when they master the skill it is remarkable how their perceptions of each other change, particularly when they realize that praise can be used to reinforce those aspects of behaviour that family members would like to see continued.

MONITORING

The case manager's role in monitoring is crucial for a number of reasons:

1. It maintains continuity of input and support for the user.
2. It allows ongoing assessment of emerging strengths and needs.
3. The outcome of linkages for service provision or other forms of support can be evaluated and recorded.
4. Efforts to correct discrepancies between assessed need and provision can be implemented at the earliest stage.
5. Shortfalls in the availability of resources to meet particular needs can be recorded and communicated to the responsible agency.

Aspects of the case manager's monitoring role have already been discussed in looking at their relationship with other agencies and carers. However, the monitoring task should be made more systematic through the use of the individual service plan. Case managers have the task of gathering together information from the user, carers, advocates, service providers and others on how the plan is proceeding. Regular reviews are required to examine the information critically and collate the views of involved parties.

At reviews the following questions can be asked of the outcomes and approaches record (described in Chapter 6):

1. Has the approach been implemented as planned?
2. If not, why not?
3. If so, did it achieve the desired outcome?
4. Is the desired outcome still relevant? Has it been superseded or did it prove to be irrelevant or inappropriate at this stage?
5. What new outcomes are sought at this point?
6. What are the corresponding approaches to each one?

Although aspects of the information-gathering side of monitoring may be assigned to other people, such as those directly involved in service provision, the case manager should retain responsibility for collating the information. Unless this is maintained, responsibility for individual service planning may be fudged, continuity of planning sacrificed and users may find themselves lost in a jungle of short-term programmes. It also avoids users being endlessly re-assessed.

The difficulty of maintaining contact with the user will depend on the case manager's involvement in direct service provision and the user's level of engagement. Here the case manager confronts the conflict between the need for assertive outreach and respect for user autonomy. Their level of assertiveness will need to be informed by the risk of the user losing contact with services and encountering dangerous crises in future. The availability of support, the user's attitude to case management services, and the way in which the user has been involved in services in the past will all be relevant. In some cases, the case manager may need to work with the user's support network, encouraging them to contact the service should early indications of problems emerge. In general, the case manager should argue for the highest amount of contact feasible that does not compromise the user's demands for autonomy. Frequent contacts may be more acceptable if they are short, informal and in the user's choice of location. They may take the form of regular phone calls or visiting the user at negotiated intervals.

EPISODIC CLOSURE

Case management is not a life sentence. Although continuity and easy access must be stressed, people may prefer to detach themselves from formal involvement with case management systems during periods of well-being. It is important, however, that closure does not occur due to arbitrary administrative reasons on the part of the service.

The golden rule regarding closure is to keep the door open for further involvement in future, particularly for people who terminate contact with the service when they are distressed or disturbed. Again, the offer of future contact should be made not only to the user but to others involved such as carers or other service providers (e.g. family doctors). They should be informed of exactly who and how to contact. Case managers should initiate contingency planning around the possibility of future problems and these plans, together with the fact that the user is no longer being formally monitored by the case management system, should be communicated to all involved, including the original referrer. A closing summary of the work undertaken by the user and case manager should be prepared in case another case manager works with the user in the future. In particular, any resource shortfalls that arose should be communicated to the relevant agencies if this has not already taken place. Ideally, closure should take place only after an individual service plan review.

Part Three

Team Working for
High-Quality Services

Chapter 9

Team working

This chapter and Chapter 10 examine team working using the EIS as a worked example, and thus assume practice as described in Part Two. The EIS offered a structure for management and day-to-day practice, and case managers had support from a resource of knowledge, experience and skill that could never exist in isolated workers. These two chapters look at the ways in which these advantages of team working can be realized.

WHAT IS A TEAM?

A recurring issue in service development work is the definition of the team. Part of the problem is a common assumption that teams can be achieved just by bringing certain people together. As a result, teams suffer crushing disillusionment when somehow sharing an office or meeting twice a week does not create a shared experience of being a team. Understanding and achieving a team requires examination of its **structure** and **process**. The team's composition, allocation of responsibilities and lines of accountability comprise its structure. Interpersonal aspects of team working and the way in which work is sequentially organized from the identification of users through to episodic closure describe its process.

Team structure

Figure 9.1 shows three commonly observed configurations of direct-care staff and their relationship to three different types of manager.

General managers (for example, general management

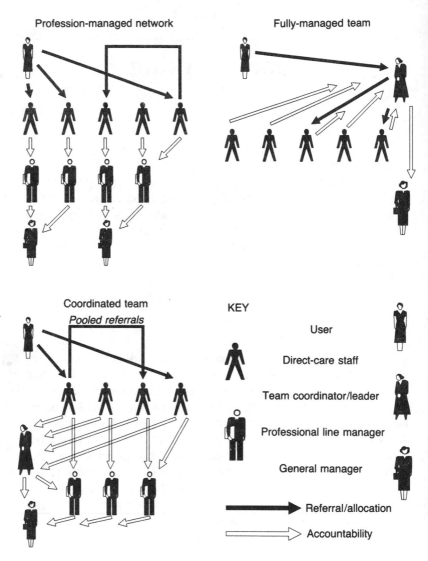

Figure 9.1 Three team structures.

within health authorities or line management within local authorities) are concerned with the overall management of the service and its resourcing. Their backgrounds are usually in administration or management.

Professional line managers are responsible for the professional supervision and monitoring of profession-specific responsibilities. They are senior practitioners of their particular profession.

Team coordinators or leaders are concerned with the day-to-day running of the service and overseeing tasks concerned with the operation of the team. Their backgrounds are likely to be more diverse but they are usually experienced practitioners based with the team. This role most closely corresponds with the role of 'care manager' described in some models of case management (e.g. Clifford and Craig, 1988). These individuals have responsibility for managing the work of case managers and may be the budget-holders for the case management service.

The profession-managed network

This is a team only in the very loosest sense. Direct-care staff remain under the control of professional line managers, and accept direct referrals. They meet with colleagues working with the same client group in the same locality but there is no team leader and often no formal requirement to attend meetings. Decisions made at meetings are not binding, and there is no collective responsibility for providing a combined service. The meetings serve to exchange information, facilitate cross-referral and sometimes to foster joint projects. The professional line managers are accountable to general management. Sometimes general managers concerned with the team are in different organizations and this inter-agency chasm prevents the network becoming more integrated.

The advantages of a network arrangement include a diversity of access points for users and a high but varying degree of professional autonomy among direct-care staff. However, there is no prioritizing of users according to need, and workers can pretty well do the work that most accords with their professional or personal skills and interests, regardless of the needs of users. Coherent monitoring of the performance of staff and outcomes for users is almost impossible as there are no shared criteria for achievement.

It is surprising how so-called multidisciplinary teams very often conform to this configuration in practice. They sometimes even have an operational policy although it is usually of merely historical interest and many people working in the network will not even know of its existence.

The fully-managed team

This might be considered the other extreme. One team leader manages all the other direct-care staff and has power to appoint, assign work, appraise performance, and discipline workers. All referrals are via the team leader. Usually the team operates by trying to achieve consensus but it is acknowledged that final accountability and authority rests with the team leader.

The fully-managed model is sometimes adopted for teams of the same discipline, or for teams of specialist case managers working in parallel with mainstream services. It has the advantages of an unambiguous referral route and coordinated allocation of work load. Strong management also permits the team to set clear priorities and evaluate its work. However, autonomy and scope for innovation on the part of individual workers are severely limited. The model is unsuitable for multidisciplinary teams where there are separate lines of professional accountability. Indeed, it is very rare for multidisciplinary teams to be managed in this way, although sometimes medically-dominated teams operate as if the senior medical member has these powers. This conflicts with general management and professional management responsibilities, and angers professional staff who feel they should enjoy greater autonomy.

The coordinated team with shared management

Here, each team member has joint accountability to both a team coordinator and their professional line manager. Each profession and their respective agencies agree on the allocation of responsibility for managing different aspects of work between the team coordinator and professional line managers (Chapter 10). Professional line managers retain responsibility for clinical supervision and have the final say on issues of clinical practice, although the team member is normally expected to be informed by the views of the team. The team coordinator remains responsible for tasks concerned with team functioning as a whole. Team coordinators may be nominated from within the team but be accountable to general management for their team coordinating responsibilities. They cannot over-ride clinical decisions but may be involved in the appointment and appraisal of staff. Some or all of the line managers connected with the team are often accountable to the same general management hierarchy as the team coordinator. Referrals are made to the team as a whole, or pooled following referral to individual team members.

The principle disadvantage of this model is complexity and the potential for conflict between the team's objectives and those of the professional line managers. However, coordinated teams offer a balance of professional autonomy against team management which, if appropriately managed, can be highly advantageous in promoting team identification and innovation. The EIS and a growing number of other mental health teams have adopted this configuration.

Other configurations

Ovretveit (1986) describes other important factors in team configuration. For example, a team may comprise core full-time members (often community mental health nurses and social workers) and part-time staff who bring a wider range of skills (e.g. psychiatrists, psychologists, occupational therapists, etc.). The core and the extended team may operate under different management arrangements.

'Joint accountability' or 'democratic' teams are another configuration. They have no single leader and assign leadership for specific aspects of team functioning when the team meets. If consensus cannot be reached on decisions a vote is taken, although these teams are usually not totally democratic as the team as a whole cannot over-ride the autonomy of individual workers within the team. Also someone would need to oversee the allocation and coordination of management tasks, which itself is a management role.

Ovretveit also describes coordinated teams where responsibility for coordinating is allocated to team members on a rotation or through periodic elections. This has the advantage of a democratic and egalitarian style but also gives rise to a number of problems. Managers and outside agencies will need to be kept abreast of who is currently coordinating the team, continuity of relationships may be sacrificed, and skills and experience acquired on the job or through training may be lost. Some team members may fear or dislike the responsibilities and the role of coordinator is more likely to become marginalized.

Team composition

There are no hard and fast rules about the composition of teams as this will depend upon the specific demands of the client group and the tasks that are undertaken within the case management service. It is, however, generally agreed that the demands on case managers are immense, and require considerable skills, knowledge and personal resources (Miller, 1983; Goldfinger et al., 1984; Berzon and Lowenstein, 1984; Kanter, 1985). Kanter (1985) recommends that case managers have experience of work with people with severe and long-term problems, an understanding of psychosocial and pharmacological interventions, knowledge of community resources, skills in assisting families with troubled relatives, an appreciation of the sociological factors affecting users and some understanding of the ways in which 'disturbed persons both shape and internalise their environmental realities'. Berzon and Lowenstein (1984) list some of the personal qualities of case managers as 'a high threshold for frustration, a high tolerance of ambiguity, an ability to measure progress in barely perceptible increments, a sense of humour, and an ability to turn to others for support' (p. 54). They also emphasize that people who will push therapy or take control of users' lives do not make suitable case managers. Goldfinger et al. (1984) suggest that case managers need to be able to show that they can respect users as they are, maintain long-term relationships with them despite disruption and frequent rejection, refuse to regard people as hopeless or untreatable, and set realistic goals for achievement.

Social workers are generally considered to be most well-qualified for case management (Huxley, 1990). For teams operating along the lines of the EIS and the Community Treatment Team in New South Wales, the involvement of community mental health nurses, clinical psychologists, occupational therapists, and administrative staff was also necessary to provide the appropriate range of skills.

Kanter (1989) suggested that case managers should be concerned wholly with environmental manipulations and separate themselves from psychiatrists who should in turn restrict themselves to biological interventions. However, the exclusion of psychiatrists from the team may impair communication over the critical issues of medication and the use of in-patient facilities. Assuming the team uses an assertive case management approach (in the manner of Stein and Test, 1980), Knoedler (1989) recommended ten hours per week of psychiatric input for every 50 users seen by the team. Given the cost of psychiatrists and their particular skills, it may not be appropriate for them to assume full case management responsibilities, but rather act as consultants to other team members by offering specialized input on assessments and planning where necessary.

Issues of responsibility and accountability

Issues of responsibility and accountability are often a source of considerable conflict within and between agencies (see Chapter 1 for definitions). This conflict stems partly from the fact that solutions can only be inferred from case law, and much remains to be legally resolved.

Mental health workers have a 'duty of care' to users. This means taking reasonable care in all circumstances through avoiding acts of negligence. These include failing to communicate important information to others involved, failing to keep abreast of recent developments in professional knowledge and practice, using highly unorthodox approaches to therapy, causing harm to the user through disclosure of information gained in the course of clinical work, and failing to preserve records intact for sufficiently long periods (Braisby *et al.*, 1988).

Professional responsibility is a narrower concept referring to those tasks that are the specific duty of each profession within the team. For example, psychologists are specifically empowered by dint of their training to conduct certain forms of psychological assessment. No one else in the team will be qualified to undertake this task or instruct the psychologist on how to do it. In English law, professional responsibility is embodied in the 'Tort of negligence' that requires professionals to recognize and observe the limits of their professional training and competence, and satisfy themselves that those to whom they refer are also appropriately qualified and competent (British Psychological Society, 1986). The professional worker cannot be held responsible for another professional's actions except in part by their own negligence in inappropriately delegating responsibility or referring on. Each profession will normally be able to refer to a code of conduct that guides the work for which they are professionally responsible.

Team members are accountable to their professional line managers for these profession-specific tasks. Although team members are expected to use the team as a resource for advice, support and supervision there is no clinical accountability to the team in any formal sense. Should there arise a situation in which the case manager felt compelled to pursue a course of action that was thought to be unwise in the team's view, the case manager should be instructed by their professional line manager. If the worker was ever accused of malpractice then peers of the same profession would be called upon to judge their actions.

Medical responsibility is often erroneously equated with 'ultimate clinical responsibility'; the notion that medical staff are ultimately responsible for the welfare of the user and so can decide the input of other staff and over-rule their decision-making. Watts and Bennett (1983) concluded that placing responsibility for deciding and coordinating the input of other workers with one individual was inappropriate because it led to inflexible service delivery, and no individual worker could realistically expect to maintain sufficient information and expertise. The British Psychological Society (1986) concluded that the whole concept of 'clinical responsibility' was too vague to be useful and drew attention to government guidance on the issue. This concluded, 'There is, as we understand it, no basis in law for the commonly expressed idea that the consultant may be held responsible for negligence on the part of others simply because he is "the responsible medical officer"; or that, though personally blameless, he may be held accountable after the style of a military commander. A multidisciplinary team has no "commander" in this sense' (Department of Health and Social Security, 1980, para. 6.17).

Medical responsibility is more properly considered as a specific example of professional responsibility; medically trained personnel are exclusively responsible for medical tasks. However, medical responsibility is complicated by the fact that it also encompasses responsibility for monitoring the health care of users, and there is no clear definition of what 'health care' entails. If taken in its broadest sense, it can be interpreted as any intervention carried out under the auspices of health services. Although this does not authorize the medically responsible team member to dictate how other workers should do their job, it does allow them to withdraw users from the care of other health workers. This cannot be over-ruled by users. In Britain people do not have a legally enshrined right to care; they only have the right to refuse it.

Medical responsibility is also complicated by the fact that aspects of it may be transferred. Family doctors hold responsibility for the overall medical welfare of their patients. When they refer to a consultant, aspects of that responsibility are delegated on the understanding that the practitioner is suitably qualified. The EIS's approach was to emphasize that medical responsibility lay with the user's family doctor who would prescribe drugs in consultation with the team psychiatrist. For those users without a family doctor or a consultant psychiatrist, the EIS psychiatrist would assume medical responsibility while efforts were made to register them with a family doctor. The team psychiatrist had access to a stock of drugs for emergencies.

Where a user was discharged from hospital under the care of a hospital-based consultant and referred to the EIS, the hospital consultant retained medical responsibility unless a transfer was negotiated with the EIS consultant. However, complications often arose over admissions as the team had no control over beds and non-hospital alternatives were not available. Since decisions on admission and discharge are usually considered as the medical responsibility of a hospital-based consultant, admissions relied on individual negotiation between the team psychiatrist and the hospital-based consultant. This produced very variable outcomes and conflicts over responsibilities concerning individual service planning while users were in hospital. In order to avoid severe discontinuity of care the case management service should retain control over hospital admission and discharge as was the case in the successful Madison service (Chapter 3).

THE PROCESS OF TEAMWORK

Hopefully, most mental health workers are more interested in working with people than reading policy documents and filling out forms. Nonetheless, some bureaucracy is necessary to help overcome ambiguity about their respective responsibilities, maintain sufficient information to effectively monitor quality, and ensure good communication. The aim is to achieve the right balance so that paperwork becomes a help rather than a hindrance.

The operational policy

Although they may differ in scope and content, in general operational policies include a statement of aims and guiding principles, describe the way the team interacts with the outside world, and describe how the team operates internally. Table 9.1 shows headings for an operational policy based upon the eighth draft operational policy of the EIS.

The functions of operational policies are to provide:

1. a reference manual for team workers on how their work should be conducted;
2. a resource for the induction of new members into the team;
3. an aid to better liaison through providing a description of the way the team relates to agencies outside the team;
4. a clear account of internal structure and process on which to base continuous team building;
5. a reference for management and those concerned with the appraisal of team performance;

Table 9.1 Sample operational policy headings

1. **Introduction**
2. **Aims of the service**
   2.1 Overall purpose
   2.2 A statement of values
   2.3 Specific service functions
3. **Personnel**
4. **Client group**
   4.1 General inclusion criteria
   4.2 General exclusion criteria
   4.3 Other criteria for prioritization
5. **Day-to-day operation**
   5.1 From referral to case management allocation
   5.1.1 Referral
   5.1.2 Planning assessment
   5.1.3 Assessment
   5.1.4 Action following assessment
   5.2. Case management
   5.2.1 Responsibilities
   5.2.2 Hospital admission in emergencies
   5.2.3 Non-urgent hospital admission
   5.2.4 Guidelines on awareness of abuse
   5.2.5 Record keeping and data collection
   5.2.6 Resources available to case managers
   5.2.7 Taking leave
   5.2.8 Prescribing drugs
   5.3 Weekly meetings
   5.3.1 Chairing
   5.3.2 The clinical review meetings
   5.3.3 The business meeting
   5.3.4 The support group
   5.4 Other activities
6. **Management and responsibility issues**
7. **Evaluation**
   Appended: Job descriptions
   Core roles and statutory
   responsibilities
   Record keeping material

6. the basis for further service development; and
7. a highly specific description of the service that can be used for public relations work and informing others interested in establishing similar services.

The operational policy has much in common with an individual service plan. It describes desired outcomes and approaches in a very specific and readable manner and if written, filed away and ignored it is totally useless. Like individual service plans, operational policies need to be part of an ongoing service review process and should be amenable to continuous revision. The document itself requires the investment of effort and ideas from members of the team and other key stakeholders, thereby maximizing consensus over the value-base, objectives and practice of the service. Research also indicates that decisions are more likely to be implemented by people who have been involved in making those decisions (Watts and Bennett, 1983). Drawing up the policy will therefore require the involvement of direct-care staff and committed individuals to lead consultation and prepare successive drafts.

The ideal situation for any team is for all its members to be recruited at the same time and to have a blank slate on which to write an operational policy. The EIS, like many demonstration projects, had this significant advantage. For most teams, however, service developments need to take account of long-standing work roles and practices, and an existing network of inter-agency relationships. Taking a fresh look at the work of an existing team in relation to the needs of its client group is much more difficult as some members are likely to have an investment in maintaining the status quo. Often the input of an outside agency may be helpful in providing structure to the process of writing the policy and maintaining an objective overview. Training packs are available that include exercises on team building and prioritizing work (e.g. Gawlinski and Graessle, 1988; Brown and Bassett, 1988).

The operational policy should commence by placing itself in context. An introduction should describe:

1. how the policy came to be written;
2. who was consulted;
3. how and when it will be reviewed;
4. how it relates to previous operational policies and strategy documents belonging to funding agents;
5. how the service fits in with other local service providers; and

6. why the policy is being written or redrafted at the present time.

What's in a name?

Finding an appropriate name for the service is no trivial matter. Witheridge and Dincin (1985) describe the importance of the naming of the Bridge project in Chicago as a means to achieving team identification and underlining its autonomy. Also, the service's user-identification function is not served through giving it a stigmatizing title (e.g. the 'psychiatric team for the homeless mentally ill').

The Early Intervention Service chose its title to reflect a particular approach to working. The decision to use the term 'service' rather than 'team' was based upon the service philosophy of the Crisis Intervention Service in Tower Hamlets, London (Waldron, 1981). An explicit policy of joint working with other agencies was advocated. Thus a 'team' came into being when a member of the 'service' and someone from an outside agency came together. The EIS pursued this policy to promote continuity of care through complementing and building on the work of existing services. In this way the EIS facilitated clinical work conducted in community settings through the provision of a resource of extra staff, enabling the dissemination of skills, and the expansion of community work undertaken by other services operating within the locality.

Aims of the service

The aims statement guides the development and practice of the service, and so much attention needs to be paid to getting it right. The aims and values of the service should be informed by similar statements made at a higher level (e.g. within a health authority – local authority joint strategy document).

It can be useful to break up the task of describing the aims of the service into a statement of the over-arching purpose of the service, the values on which these are based, and the more specific functions which the service aims to carry out in the execution of its overall purpose. Patton (1986) draws a useful distinction between 'outcome goals' – the outcomes that the team's activity is aiming to achieve – and 'activity goals' which describe what the service will do to achieve those desired outcomes. For the EIS the overall purpose (and outcome goal) of the team was to: 'Maintain people experiencing mental health problems within their community, among the people they find supportive, and in the places in which they reside, spend time during the day and engage in recreation'. The values and beliefs that underlined this were stated in the policy as:

1. People with mental health problems have a need and a right to a lifestyle that would be valued by other members of society.
2. Services should aim to preserve these valued aspects of lifestyle.
3. Choosing and using ordinary, non-stigmatizing services are valued aspects of lifestyle.
4. People should be offered help in the social, familial and physical context in which they are experiencing difficulties.
5. It is the responsibility of services to respond flexibly to the needs of individuals with mental health problems.
6. Services need to be proactive: establishing needs and becoming maximally relevant and accessible to potential client groups.
7. High-quality continuous care is facilitated by joint working, attention to communication between agencies and clarity regarding roles and responsibilities.

The statement of aims goes on to describe in more detail the idea of 'early intervention' as a model of practice embodying a stress-vulnerability approach to mental distress. Its activity goals were:

1. To conduct clinical work with individuals or families who are experiencing severe stress or failure to cope within their social context, working jointly and intensively with existing services.
   Wherever possible this provided an alternative to hospital admission.
2. To develop problem-orientated programmes for the pre-vention or resolution of clinical, social, family or occupa-

tional problems that may increase vulnerability to episodes of distress.

This work was conducted alongside workers from other agencies and informal carers. It would include helping the user to establish a supportive network of contacts through liaison with other agencies, behavioural family therapy to increase effective family problem-solving and improve communication, and developing a contingency plan with hostel staff should a resident enter an episode of disturbed behaviour.

3. To provide community-based assessment involving carers and other significant people.

   This would include, for example, assessment of home management skills in a hostel by a community occupational therapist.

4. To help establish groups or other services aimed at minimizing distress in community settings working jointly with existing agencies.

5. To continuously monitor and evaluate the service provided.

6. To train other workers (e.g. clinical psychology trainees, student social workers, student nurses, medical students, nurses, junior doctors, voluntary workers and informal carers).

7. To provide opportunities for research relating to aspects of care in the community.

Activity goals should be prioritized in order to achieve clarity over how team members should be spending their time. Although the aims statement should describe activity goals, it is important that the over-riding emphasis is given to the expected outcomes for service users since these provide the main criteria against which performance should be evaluated.

Client group

The importance of clarity in this regard is essential in order to determine the success of the team in serving particular groups. Prioritization is necessary for appropriate gatekeeping (vertical target efficiency) and communication to outside agencies and the local population about who the team is for (horizontal target efficiency). *Caring for People* (Cm 849, 1989) advocated priority being given to those whose needs would be most costly to provide for. However, although they are most likely to be people with complex needs, this may have the effect of prioritizing according to features of services rather than individuals seeking assistance. Eligibility criteria should aim to include those most in need of services, based upon information on the assessed needs of the local population and existing service provision.

One difficulty in determining priorities is that people do not fall neatly into categories and so a range of criteria may need to be employed. Usually there will be general inclusion criteria covering whether the individual lives within the team's catchment area and is within the required age range. If there are other criteria for inclusion which clarify the client group they should also be included. For example, the EIS found it was helpful to state that the service was both for people experiencing their first episode of craziness and those with past or present contact with mental health services.

The policy should also state at the outset who the team does not serve. For the EIS general exclusion criteria included a clear need for immediate hospital admission, and drug or alcohol dependency as a primary problem. Non-clinicians should be able to screen according to general inclusion and exclusion criteria at the point of referral and they should be equipped with information on alternative sources of assistance for those people being excluded. Guidance on screening and different levels of assessment is available (Social Services Inspectorate, 1991).

Further criteria are necessary to meaningfully prioritize cases. The services described in Chapter 3 used eligibility criteria such as history and frequency of past admissions, diagnosis and housing status. However, these were often used for research purposes, and most services may not have enough information available to make such fine discriminations. The EIS used three dimensions in descending order of priority: severity and urgency; reported mental state; and a need for home-based intervention. People included under the 'severity and urgency' criterion were presenting in extreme distress or disorder, but in the opinion of the referrer their problems could be contained until an assessment on the day of referral or the day after. Excluded under this dimension were people for whom a statutory assessment for admission to hospital was clearly necessary immediately. At the other end of this continuum, users who were not in immediate distress or disorder and who could wait for an appointment with another agency were also not assessed. For example, users referred with problems relating to a long-standing anxiety state were usually redirected towards the District Psychology Service.

Under the 'mental state' dimension, priority was given to individuals who would be diagnosed as suffering from a major mental disorder (such as schizophrenia).

Finally, under the 'need for community-based assessment' criterion, priority was given to users who would be unable or unlikely to attend for an appointment at a clinic. Examples include people known to be non-attenders, or people prevented from leaving their home by physical or psychological problems. Community-based assessments were also thought to be more appropriate for people with poor access to services due to social inequalities. This included people from ethnic minorities who may understandably perceive services run by predominantly white, middle-class workers as having little relevance to them. Homeless people living in bed-and-breakfast accommodation or with no fixed abode were also considered for the same reasons. The aim was that community-based assessments should at least remove some of the barriers to accessing assistance.

This approach to prioritization was sophisticated enough to keep the service on track but flexible enough to accept exceptional individuals that the team could usefully serve. For example, although a user with severe anxiety but no indications or history of major mental disorder would score low on the 'mental state' dimension, this was countered by scoring high on the 'need for a community-based assessment' if that anxiety prevented them from leaving the house.

Day-to-day operation

Figure 9.2 shows the process of referrals to the EIS. The following describes each stage.

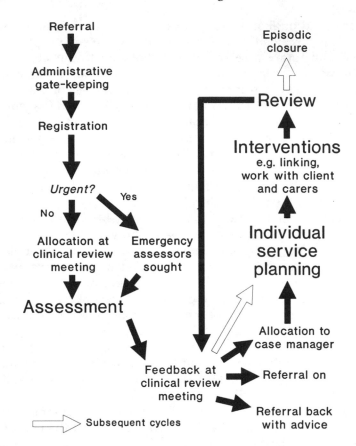

Figure 9.2 The process of work with users of the EIS.

Referral

In the interests of maximum accessibility, the most assertive form of identification of users and the most open system of referral may be desirable. Outreach work may take the form of personally approaching people who are acting in a crazy way (such as Project Reach Out in New York), piggy-backing services on other forms of service provision (such as the Skid Row Mental Health Service in Los Angeles), providing an accessible drop-in service, or liaising closely with a range of agencies to encourage the referral of particular client groups.

When targeting specific client groups it may be appropriate to focus attention on one referral source. For example, one London-based team concentrated all their attention on attracting referrals from hostels for single homeless men (Psychiatric Team for Single Homeless People, 1990). The extent of the referral net may also be shaped by existing relationships between providers. The EIS adopted a strategy of identifying referral sources that were in contact with the target client group but that were not already well served by other agencies.

Self-referrals and referrals by carers should be encouraged, although it is imperative to have alternative suggestions available if the referral does not fulfil eligibility criteria since they may have no other supports currently available.

The actual process of referral should be made as easy as possible while retaining the advantages of a single access point. By offering referral by phone the EIS found that referral by letter was almost eliminated. This had the advantage of offering an opportunity to collect a lot of information at an early stage but demanded a skilled administrator to systematically record the information required to screen out referrals that did not fulfil general criteria. Sometimes the receipt of referral was handed over to a clinician if there was some ambiguity about the nature of the request. An answerphone took messages out of office hours which were responded to by the administrator as soon as possible.

Initial information and planning
If the referral met general criteria, registration details were collected in order to plan assessment. Checks were made to determine whether the case was known to existing mental health services in order to avoid intervening in the work of other agencies. For example, where a case was already under a consultant team, an assessment was only carried out on the invitation of the relevant consultant, unless a family doctor had specifically requested EIS involvement. In this latter case, the relevant consultant team was notified with the aim of involving workers from that team in assessment and any subsequent planning regarding the case.

At referral, referrers were asked whether they would like to be involved in the assessment. They were also asked if the user

was aware that they had been referred. The referrer was asked
to let the user know of the referral unless it would be a significant handicap to ever getting to meet the user.

For urgent referrals, the administrator endeavoured to make
contact with an EIS worker by pager or phone, unless a clinical review meeting was scheduled for later that day. Urgent
referrals were defined as those where the referrer felt the user
should be seen on that or the following day. Most cases were
taken to a clinical review meeting for allocation for assessment.

Allocation for assessment

Allocation of the referral for assessment was determined by
the extent to which the needs of the user corresponded to the
skills, experience, ethnic origin, gender and interests of the
worker. This was in order to increase the quality and relevance
of the assessment and preserve continuity. It is preferable for
the worker who carries out the assessment to become the
user's case manager should they continue contact with the
service.

Using the assessment

On the basis of the assessment, an initial management plan
was drafted by the assessors. At the next clinical review meeting they reported on the assessment and their plans to the
team. This is perhaps the most critical stage of the therapeutic
intervention and usually requires in-depth discussion. Other
involved workers and carers can be invited. There are three
possible outcomes to this initial planning: immediate referral to
a more appropriate agency, referral back to the referrer with
advice, or allocation to a case manager.

Allocation for case management

At the EIS any profession within the team could assume case
management responsibility. This responsibility could be subsequently transferred to another member of the team if necessary, and its assumption by one profession did not exclude
input from other team members.

Within the EIS operational policy, the role of case managers was described as a mixture of clinical and team tasks.
Specifically their responsibilities were to:

1. Seek out any further information needed following initial assessment.

   This may be via old notes, communication with the referrer, or others involved.

2. Send a letter or report to the referrer describing the outcome of the assessment.

3. Arrange any further assessments.

   For example, a psychiatric or occupational therapy assessment from within the team.

4. Establish with the user a collaborative approach aimed at achieving the outcomes that they have identified.

   It was sometimes useful to negotiate a contract with the user.

5. Report any relevant information regarding assessments and subsequent developments to the other team members at clinical review meetings, the referrer, the user's family doctor and any other workers involved.

6. Organize clinical reviews.

   The first review occurred within six weeks after allocation and other people involved with the case were invited. Subsequent reviews occurred not more than six weeks later. Extra reviews were organized as necessary and for some complex and difficult cases this happened frequently.

7. Actively seek the involvement of other workers or agencies in helping to meet any of the various needs that the user identifies.

   This included drawing on resources both within and outside the team.

8. Hand over and liaise with relevant staff when individuals are admitted to hospital or become engaged by another agency.

   If the case was to remain open, reviews and case conferences were attended, links with relatives and friends were maintained, and the case manager remained available to help transfer the user back to a less sheltered environment.

9. Inform the clinical review meetings of any delays or refusals in gaining assessments information or treatments.

10. Inform the coordinator, the relevant line manager or the team as a whole of any concerns about finding oneself

unable to cope with any aspect of the work, including personal difficulties, unrealistic demands on experience and knowledge, or sheer volume of work.

There was always a danger of the team assuming a 'macho' culture in which case managers suffer in silence for fear of being thought inadequate. Since everyone has a unique but finite range of skills, knowledge and experience, case managers should be applauded for acknowledging any limitations.

11. Arrange all appointments and room bookings to end before 7 pm.

   This emerged as necessary to help team members maintain boundaries around their working hours.

12. Ensure that records are kept up to date.

13. Ensure that data for evaluation are clearly communicated to the administrator for entry onto computer.

14. When taking leave, legibly summarize work to date in the notes, including any necessary contingency plans should the user encounter difficulties in the case manager's absence.

   If another worker needed to be involved, this was made explicit in the summary and agreed with the worker concerned. Cases were also summarized verbally at a clinical review meeting.

15. Phase down involvement when approaching closure on a case, maintaining contact with a user until they have found alternative support.

   Where a user was being referred back to the original referrer or another agency, the case manager met with them in order to decide how to respond to any early warning signs of relapse or other difficulties. This stage particularly involved unpaid carers and stressed that the EIS could be called on again at any time (unless it was agreed that this would not be appropriate).

16. Ensure that the original referrer (and the family doctor) has a written record stating that the case is closed and including any contingency planning.

17. Carry an ID card on all home visits and produce it on demand.

Involvement of non-EIS persons was ongoing during the case management process, and following episodic closure, users could be re-referred for further EIS involvement at any stage. They would normally work with the same case manager as before.

Guidelines on liaising with other agencies
The operational policy should contain guidelines for case managers on local arrangements for assessment for emergency admission to hospital or the planned use of other services. This should include guidance on who to consult and how they can be contacted. For example, at the EIS all case managers followed guidelines on awareness of child abuse when working with families. The EIS social workers did not assume statutory child care responsibilities and any outstanding statutory child care duties were passed directly to the relevant hospital or area social work team.

Record-keeping and data collection
Record-keeping is crucial to developing an expanding picture of the user's needs and strengths, and is also important for the ongoing evaluation of the work of the team. The EIS used record forms covering registration, assessment, action and subsequent contact after the first closure. A file for every individual or family contained the forms, handwritten notes summarizing the work done and any correspondence. These files were centrally and securely located at the team's administrative base. The availability of records was essential for good communication between agencies and covering for case managers during absences. It was the responsibility of case managers to pursue information and ensure that records were up-to-date and available.

A computer-based case register of information from the record forms was constantly updated and expanded. The availability of expensive computer hardware is often regarded as an obstacle to developing record systems. In practice the requirements may be minimal: an IBM-compatible personal computer with a hard disc of at least 20 megabyte capacity, some means of establishing the security of backed-up data, and user-

friendly software that allows the easy entry of data while maintaining security of access to information via the terminal. Some
services design their own systems using off-the-shelf data-base
packages (EIS, 1989; Sherman, 1989) but more elaborate systems are available (Chapter 6). A desirable feature is that the
design of the form should match the screens on which the data
is entered via computer.

Weekly meetings

The proper management of weekly meetings is essential to the
smooth running of the team. The operational policy should
describe the time and place for each meeting, their purpose,
and format. The EIS operated three types of meeting: a twice-
weekly clinical review meeting, a weekly business meeting and
a weekly staff support group. The clinical review meetings
aimed 'To provide peer supervision and support to case managers in the execution of their work . . . [and] a forum for
involving other workers'. A list of ongoing cases was circulated
at the beginning of each meeting which included dates of
referral, assessment and review. The agenda comprised:

1. discussion of new referrals or re-referrals, and allocation as
   appropriate;
2. feedback from assessments and the planning of subsequent
   action;
3. discussion of cases awaiting assessment. This often included
   people that were proving difficult to find or engage;
4. update on ongoing cases. Brief feedback was given on
   progress by case managers. This allowed opportunities
   for monitoring progress, peer supervision and support,
   and brainstorming on any particular obstacles that were
   presenting;
5. reviews. Time for this part of the meeting was rigorously
   defended and involved an in-depth scheduled review of one
   or two cases. The outcomes/approaches record form was
   used as the basis of reviews.

The clinical review meetings and the business meetings
were chaired by all members of the team on a one-month
rotation. The rotation of chair was a tangible demonstration

of the egalitarian and non-hierarchical nature of the team. Chairpersons needed a clear format and considerable support from other members of the team to achieve the successful management of heavy agendas and vociferous participants.

The EIS was not successful in regularly involving users and carers in clinical review meetings. Time pressure precluded attending to features of the meeting that would allow the users or carers to participate on equal terms with team members. As it could not be done well it was decided not to do it at all, thereby placing an even greater emphasis on the need for a collaborative and empowering approach to the decision-making that went on outside the clinical review meetings.

Resources available to case managers

It is important to identify resources available to case managers for the execution of their duties particularly when operational policy is used for the induction of new members to the team. For example, the EIS case managers had access to directories of other services, a leased car, and a computer package to help determine the welfare benefits that users were entitled to (Blackwell and Jarman, 1991).

Other activities

The foregoing has been concerned with the priority functions of the team. The operational policy should also spell out those other activities that serve the overall aims of the service such as the training and supervision of other staff, consultation to specific agencies, liaison and publicity work, group work, case managers' own further training, representation on community or planning groups, and project-orientated research activity.

Interpersonal aspects of team working

Helping workers find a recognized place in the team

The social psychology of group work suggests that group members identify most strongly with the group when it has clear objectives (Sherif, 1966), and they can clearly perceive their respective roles in the achievement of those objectives (Deschamps and Brown, 1983; Brown and Wade, 1987). In team working this requires that case managers have a clear understanding of the aims of the service as a whole, and their colleagues' particular skills and special areas of responsibility in achieving those goals. The British Psychological Society (1986) recommend a skills audit within the team to highlight skills, knowledge and experience pertaining to:

1. required practices arising from legislation (e.g. the approved social worker's role in formal assessments under the Mental Health Act 1983);
2. restricted practices arising from professional qualifications (e.g. the role of doctors in prescribing drugs);
3. 'core' skills that would be expected of particular professions even though they may not be formally restricted to any one group (e.g. the role of occupational therapists in assessments of activities of daily living skills);
4. basic skills shared by several professions (e.g. interviewing skills);
5. special skills and qualifications acquired through individual interest and training (e.g. family therapy, or hypnosis).

The roles of individuals within the team can be seen as a set of overlapping domains. The object is to separate areas of overlap from tasks that are part of the core, restricted and statutory responsibilities that are unique to each profession. Table 9.2 represents these 'bare bones' of the professional roles as perceived by members of the EIS. A separate audit of the skills, knowledge and experience of post-holders described areas where skills overlapped. This information can usefully be gained through team-building exercises and provides an up-to-date account of the resources available within the team as a whole.

Staff support

The need for staff support comes from a number of directions. Offices, desks, uniforms (such as collars and ties) and language serve as a powerful defence against fully appreciating the

Table 9.2 Core tasks and statutory responsibilities of team members

The administrator
- Receiving referrals by phone.
- Performing clerical duties regarding clinical case material.
- Entering data onto computer.

The social worker
- Carrying out statutory duties under the Mental Health Act 1983 (and the Child Care Acts where necessary).
- Negotiations to ensure basic material security (i.e. accommodation, income, etc.).

The consultant psychiatrist
- Making statutory recommendations under the Mental Health Act.
- To liaise with family doctor on appropriate drug therapy and advise on the detection of early signs of psychotic breakdown
- To assume medical responsibility in cases where the user has no family doctor or is not already under the care of a consultant psychiatrist.
- In cases where the user is already under a consultant, to liaise with that consultant before taking any medical action.

The occupational therapist
- Practical assessments of activities of daily living: home management, self-care, work, and leisure skills.
- Design of programmes addressing the above.

The clinical psychologist
- Assessment and programme design for severe behavioural problems.
- Psychometric testing.

The community mental health nurse
- Carrying out prescribed medical treatments.
- Advising on the need for further medical assessment.

experience of people with severe and long-term mental health problems. Involved and continuous community-based work removes these defences and exposes case managers to high levels of distress and the often miserable circumstances in which people live. In the same way that users need support in dealing with problems of living, the case manager will in turn need support in dealing with the feelings that may be engendered though close involvement in users' lives. Otherwise they run the risk of employing psychological defences which will impede their work, such as 'blaming the victim'.

Stress also derives from the public nature of case management. Workers are required to share their work with colleagues and account for their activities. Linking requires that case managers have a high profile among other agencies and they may even come under scrutiny through external evaluation or staff appraisal.

Leiter (1988) examined burn-out in multidisciplinary mental health teams and its relationship to work-orientated inter-actions (e.g. supervision, consultation, administration) and informal social support (e.g. friendships, non-work orientated interaction). Burn-out was associated with low job satisfaction and the maintenance of relatively few informal supportive contacts with co-workers. A high number of work-related contacts with co-workers increased feelings of accomplishment but may also have contributed to emotional exhaustion. Informal contact was related both to higher levels of accomplishment and job satisfaction. The study concluded that there is a need for management to create work settings that 'utilize those aspects of work-orientated communication that enhance feelings of accomplishment, while minimizing the demands and drudgery that aggravate exhaustion'. In short, teams should have no qualms about trying to enjoy themselves. For example, at the EIS, periodic service reviews were accompanied by a social event that was as unrelated to work as possible.

One unhelpful reaction to the demands of the job observed within the EIS seemed to be a form of addiction to accomplish-ment in which the enthusiasm and energy of team members was translated into a 'macho' team culture where case man-agers took on increasing amounts of work, and boundaries around hours worked broke down. In view of this and the attendant dangers of exhaustion and burn-out, it is important to establish a culture where the seeking of support is highly valued. Although this can be communicated through individ-ual supervision, within the EIS a support group was found to be the most effective vehicle.

The aim of the support group was to provide an opportunity for team members to discuss any matters of concern with the team as a whole. These matters were of a more personal nature than those discussed in business meetings. The meeting was weekly and took place over lunch. Attendance was compulsory for full-time staff and students (unless on placement for less than three months). The meeting could not be interrupted (e.g. by pagers) and if anyone was to be more than five minutes late they were asked not to interrupt the meeting. The content of the meeting was not discussed outside the team.

The support meeting became the most sacrosanct meeting of the week and central to team functioning. Debate over whether to involve an outside facilitator resulted in an outside facilitator coming along to tell the team that they did not need one! The emphasis was on interpersonal problem-solving and was highly permissive. Aside from the boundaries described above there was no structure and any one meeting might be an hour of uninterrupted hilarity, a relaxed chat over lunch or intense and draining problem resolution. Compulsory attendance at the meeting prevented unresolvable splits emerging within the team.

Managing conflict

Internal conflict is a normal and necessary aspect of team working. It is important that it is not avoided but managed. Teams that are over-concerned with appearing cohesive may cease to attend to information that conflicts with the team's assumptions, and strong social pressure is brought to bear on people that question the status quo (Watts and Bennett, 1983). Sometimes teams become overcohesive as a result of hostility from outside the team, leading to a situation where anyone who opposes the beliefs or practices of the team simply becomes an enemy to be ignored or overcome (Gibson, 1989). Adopting this stance stifles innovation and the productive development of the service (Chapter 11).

Conflict may take the form of interpersonal difficulties within the team, or situations where the demands from a team member's line management conflict with the role and philosophy of the team. Smooth running of the team process requires a clear mechanism for achieving resolution in cases of dissent or dispute within the team. At the EIS, the coordinator, the support group and a management steering group comprised a mechanism for resolution. The steering group advised the general manager with ultimate responsibility for managing the team and included the coordinator and professional line managers among its members.

The mechanism for resolution comprised a series of 'back-stops'. First, the coordinator approached the team member or members concerned and encouraged them to make use of the support group. However, if this was not appropriate or if they refused and resolution could not be achieved within the team, the coordinator liaised with the appropriate line manager to attempt a solution. Where this was unsatisfactory, the co-ordinator took the problem to the general manager with overall responsibility, who had the option of calling upon the team's steering group as a forum for attempting resolution. In practice, conflict only ever had to be taken outside the support group on one occasion. This is fortunate since successful problem-solving within the team appeared to promote team identification and a sense of autonomy.

Chapter 10

Managing case management

Chapter 9 described the type of managers involved with the team and different approaches to team structure. This chapter looks more closely at team management assuming a coordinated team approach.

Ovretveit (1986) argued that a clear team leader role is essential to close and effective teamwork and highlighted a common tendency to avoid addressing interprofessional and inter-agency conflicts by simply choosing not to consider team management issues. What may be termed 'flexible management' or 'room to manoeuvre' may actually represent ambiguity arising from lack of leadership at higher levels and procrastination for fear of upsetting anyone. This sacrifices effective team functioning for an easy life in the short term.

ALLOCATION OF MANAGEMENT TASKS

Ovretveit offered a definition of levels of managerial authority. In descending order of power they are:

1. the right to decide, whereby one party can over-rule the views of others;
2. joint decision-making power, whereby each party has power of veto; and
3. the right to be informed or consulted.

The team coordinator and professional line managers need to establish their authority on a range of tasks, and members of the general management hierarchy may need to be involved in the process of defining roles. Within a coordinated team structure, responsibility for managing professional practice lies with professional line managers while team management responsibilities are allocated to the team coordinator (Chapter 9). Nonetheless, consensus on how this translates in practice should not be assumed and the management of tasks should be clearly allocated. These tasks include drafting job descriptions, shortlisting job applicants, interviewing and appointing, defining the client group, allocating cases, reviewing work load, appraising annual performance, organizing training, coordinating leave and expenses, and disciplining direct-care staff.

The integrity of the team will rely largely on the balance of allocation of responsibility to the team coordinator or professional line management. If, for example, professional line managers are empowered to allocate work to team members, relocate them or redefine their client group the team may become rapidly degraded into a loosely connected network of direct-care staff. Ovretveit advocates assigning as much authority as possible to the team coordinator with professional managers acting in an advisory role. The following describes the role of team coordinator, drawing upon the practice of the EIS.

TEAM COORDINATION

In Chapter 9 we saw how the coordinator has no formal managerial power to instruct other workers on how to practise their profession. This would correspond to the unqualified assumption of 'ultimate clinical responsibility' described in Chapter 9. Instead, the role of coordinator involves managing the mechanics of team functioning, orientating team members towards the correct mechanisms for support, supervision and conflict resolution and acting as an interface between the team and management. They are accountable for these tasks to a general management hierarchy or a joint board authorized to manage the team by a number of agencies (Chapter 4). If the coordinator also carries out professional duties (as in the EIS) they remain accountable to their professional hierarchy for clinical work.

The tasks of coordination can be divided up into those concerned with day-to-day team functioning, service development, and interfacing with management.

Day- to-day team functioning

Administrative aspects

It is necessary that the operational policy is kept alive through being used in the everyday running of the team. The mechanical aspects of team functioning, such as methods for receiving referrals, managing case loads and running meetings, cannot be properly evaluated unless the agreed procedures are carried out in the first place. Here the coordinator has the job of bringing procedures to the attention of workers and ensuring that the team functions as planned.

Personnel aspects

One aspect of the coordinator's role in managing the day-to-day operation is in the prevention of burn-out through ensuring that team members are clear about their role, and facilitating staff support. The latter may involve a personal one-to-one contact, or encouragement to make use of existing structures such as professional line management or a team support group.

It is unusual for team coordinators to be empowered to discipline staff as this will normally be the responsibility of professional line managers. However, coordinators may be formally authorized to approach team members to demand that they seek professional support or, should this fail, liaise with their line managers directly. In order to promote team morale and identification, it is clearly preferable not to rely on line managers for the resolution of every dispute, and a system of progressive back-stops should be clearly identified within the team. Coordinators need to be very clear about those situations that demand the authority of professional line managers or general managers on personnel issues.

The administrative and personnel aspects may overlap. For example, the EIS coordinator's role in monitoring case loads involved devoting a weekly slot to ascertaining with individual team members the number of cases that they were carrying, the nature of the cases and any difficulties that the worker was encountering. If the case manager was having problems or was under undue strain, they were encouraged to bring this up in supervision with their line manager, or highlight the problems at a clinical review meeting or support group.

Service development

Leading policy development

The coordinator will usually be leading the drawing up and review of the team's operational policy. The process of drafting material, consultation and review should be structured to maximize the involvement of key stake-holders and team members. Often the coordinator will act as a spokesperson for the team among local service providers and managers, describing the aims and practice of the service and seeking to discover how this fits in with others concerned. The coordinator should be able to rely heavily on support from the general management hierarchy in performing this function both in terms of resources and an over-arching agency statement about what the service should be achieving for people.

Staff induction and ongoing training

The involvement of the whole team in the continuous development of the operational policy can provide a vehicle for staff induction and team building. Other induction programmes and team-based training may also be needed. For example, priority setting, audits of the skills and talents of team members, and exercises aimed at clarifying respective roles and responsibilities can usefully take place at critical points in the team's development, such as following major changes in direction or composition. Although outside agencies may be contracted in to assist with training, the coordinator will be ideally placed to assess training needs within the team.

Evaluation

Key stakeholders, such as general managers and people concerned with monitoring the quality of the service, will need information to make important decisions about the service. The evaluation may be of a 'pass or fail' nature (e.g. 'Does the service merit further funding next year?') or aim to inform service development (e.g. 'How might the service meet the needs of its identified client group more effectively and efficiently?'). As overseer of the administrative aspects of team working, the coordinator is well placed to help stakeholders identify the information they need and lead evaluation.

The service's outcome and activity goals comprise the standards against which the service is evaluated. Evaluating activity goals involves determining the extent to which the team is acting in the way described in the operational policy. For example, is the team really working with users with severe and long-term mental health problems and offering joint assessment to all referrers? The more challenging question is whether the service is achieving desirable outcomes for users. We shall return to this question in Chapter 11. Suffice to say the task of evaluating the team's work will be made easier if the work of the team can be adequately recorded and monitored with the help of computers. Coordinators have a role in consulting on the design of information systems to ensure that they are workable and useful to the service. They also have the job of overseeing the office management duties to ensure that records are adequately and continuously kept day-to-day.

Interfacing with management

Coordinators provide a single and accessible point of contact between the team and general management, and a resource for maintaining an effective working relationship between team members and their line managers. As with case management itself, the single contact point allows greater personal involvement and continuity of interest and the coordinator can act as a conduit for information going in all directions.

Acting on behalf of the team

The coordinator has the task of ensuring that managers are kept abreast of the work of the team and the team's perspective on the changing demands of its target population. The coordinator is responsible for communicating any problems with resources or the practice of case management as stipulated in the operational policy. This will draw on data used in evaluation and the coordinator will normally take the lead in summarizing and reporting the results. The content of reports may have enormous implications for the service so any co-ordinator should be very clear about the aims of the report and the demands of its audience. For example, does the report aim to provide a definitive account of the minutiae of operations comprising the work of a case management team, a political statement about unmet need for services within urban areas, or a justification for another six months' funding? Is the audience to be a single management group or are the achievements of the team to be broadcast more widely for further consultation? Is there scope for publication? Will the target audience realistically extend its attention span beyond three or four pages? Is there a need for different types of report or perhaps a punchy summary? The more people the coordinator can consult in answering these difficult questions the better.

Acting on behalf of individuals

The coordinator's role in conflict resolution extends beyond the team. For example, where there are conflicting demands on a worker from the team and their line manager, the coordinator may usefully intercede at the request of the worker. If this is unsuccessful and the worker remains in an untenable position, the coordinator may need to raise the issue with general management. The coordinator may also be involved in supporting the worker in feeding back to their line manager about handicapping shortfalls in resources administered by that line manager. For example, time and money to meet a worker's specific training needs.

Communicating information from management

It is important that information on the availability of resources and policy constraints are communicated to the team. This information will naturally come via the coordinator. Where this can be construed as acting on behalf of management the coordinator is likely to experience some role conflict. It may need to be made very clear that coordinators are only responsible for communicating information, and should not be expected to advocate a particular policy or approach on behalf of management.

Summary

To summarize and offer an example, the EIS coordinator's job description included the following:

Service level

1. Promoting the development and operation of the EIS in accordance with the aims described in the operational policy.
2. Facilitating internal and external conflict resolution.
3. Organizing team reviews of practice and policy.
4. On behalf of EIS members, reporting to management any problems over resource allocation, liaison with other agencies, ancillary services or professional practice.
5. Communicating important information from general management.
6. Representing the team at the steering group and other planning groups or public meetings. Ensuring that data for evaluation are available. Compiling annual reports on the EIS and preparing interim reports for the steering group or other planning groups when requested.

Administrative level

1. Supervising the team administrator and office management functions.
2. Coordinating annual and study leave in order to avoid more than two clinicians being away at any one time.
3. Signing team members' leave and expenses forms as agreed with their respective line managers.

Case level

1. Ensuring that all ongoing cases are allocated to a case manager.
2. Overseeing case load.

Establishing an optimal culture for committed teamwork

Team coordinators are well placed to facilitate improved team working through adopting an appropriate leadership style. Provencal (1987) warns against autocratic reigns of terror or leaders who hoard knowledge, power and credit for team successes. Instead he suggests that team leaders should communicate clear and attainable team objectives and promote a sense that all team members are 'part of the chase'. Team members should be helped to feel good about the work they are doing through underlining the positive impact they are having on individuals' lives.

There seems to be a popular culture of cynicism among mental health workers in which idealism equates with naivety. A sense of hopelessness arises from the apparently over-determined social conditions of users, and the self-interested political machinations of so-called helping agencies. Cynicism benefits neither the team's morale nor users. Acknowledging difficulties while being involved in team members' successes and failures and complimenting colleagues on their work are simple but immensely effective ways of improving morale that can be undertaken by all team members.

It is also important to establish an atmosphere in which the difficulty of the work can be discussed in order to avoid the insidious 'macho' culture described previously. The team co-ordinator can model expressions of inadequacy, helplessness or fatigue as inherent aspects of being 'professional', and so underline that every team member has a unique but finite set of skills.

Watts and Bennett (1983) emphasize the importance of team leaders being available, approachable and able to understand various viewpoints within the team. A key indicator of success in this area is the coordinator's attitude towards the 'least preferred co-worker'. They should feel equally valued and not oppressed or excluded by power wielded by the coordinator.

What makes a good coordinator?

The coordinator's single most important qualification is credibility in the eyes of other team members. Such credibility derives from perceived personal competence, whether the candidate was chosen by the team or imposed from outside, and the extent to which they visibly adhere to the norms and values of the team (Hollander, 1978). A candidate will have a clear advantage if they demonstrate good practice, carry a case load and have been involved in the development of the service. Significantly, the EIS coordinators have been drawn from the longest-serving team members.

The fostering of an optimal culture for committed team work relies heavily on the practice of the coordinator, rather than their professional background. However, many of the skills required are those of the trainer. An understanding of learning theory and natural systems is advantageous and psychologists are clearly well-endowed with these skills. However, they do not hold a monopoly and coordinators can be drawn from any professional background. Perhaps the only profession that may be ill-suited is medicine. This is not a criticism of the personality characteristics of medical practitioners but rather a wariness concerning the roles they are often expected to perform in teams. Unwittingly, the behaviour of outside agencies, and even team members who are used to working in medically-dominated hospital-based teams, creates the expectation that the team psychiatrist will be the ultimate arbiter on clinical decisions. The assumption of ultimate clinical responsibility is illegitimate, and can create confusion and conflict (Chapter 9). Where this is confused with a poorly-defined leadership role, the situation is doubly calamitous. Since an egalitarian culture is important to team working (Chapter 11), and not every medical person will have the will-power to resist such pressures, it may be better not to place them in the vulnerable position of team coordinator. The decline in doctors occupying leadership positions in the US was lamented by Jabitsky (1988) who outlined the options for psychiatrists as 'submit, fight or flee'. Hopefully, as responsibility for mental health service delivery becomes more devolved and decentralized, British psychiatrists will feel able to adopt a constructive approach to changes in their role that ensures the continued availability of their unique skills.

A final ingredient for the making of a good coordinator is that they should feel valued themselves. Inflexible pay scales have meant that there are no recognized mechanisms for extra payment for added responsibility. Leadership functions thus become marginalized and compete for time with normal clinical duties. This situation may improve with sections of district health authorities achieving trust status as a result of the NHS and Community Care Act (1990). Considering the centrality of the coordinator role for the burgeoning case management and community mental health team movement, the issue of team coordination merits more attention and resources.

THE TASKS OF GENERAL MANAGEMENT

General management is primarily concerned with maintaining the service on course, resourcing and broader strategy issues. The coordinator may answer to an individual within the general management hierarchy or to a joint board comprising managers from a variety of agencies. A joint board is suitable for case management services that involve workers from a range of agencies or where the service primarily serves facilities managed by other agencies. If a joint board is adopted it will be crucial that the process for decision-making within it is clearly defined and it may be advantageous to identify a member of the joint board who carries ultimate management responsibility. This gives the coordinator one individual to liaise with. The EIS had a steering group comprising line managers from all the disciplines involved, a family doctor representing primary care, representatives of the local Community Health Council and MIND group, the coordinator and a general manager carrying ultimate responsibility. The group acted in an advisory capacity to the general manager who was responsible for managing the coordinator's responsibilities.

The position of this manager within their own hierarchy will be crucial. Linking with the top of the hierarchy may be advantageous in terms of access to power but may suffer due to the lack of personal involvement that the manager can offer the team. For a developing service it may be advantageous to link with a manager who is not overconcerned with maintaining the status quo, and is well connected with other important parts of the provider system. The EIS was fortunate in linking with a member of the health authority general management structure who was responsible for managing other local health service providers working in the same field, and who had good links with corresponding managers in the local social services department. Such connections may be invaluable in preventing the team becoming isolated or marginalized among other agencies.

The role of general management in managing coordinated teams is that of enabler rather than director. Like professional line managers, general managers may undermine the autonomy of the team through assuming too much control over day-to-day operation. However, they should assume enough control to intervene where the coordinator is failing to deliver the required service in accordance with agreed aims. In concert with professional line managers, they should also retain enough authority to hire and fire team members in order to ensure the team is able to fulfil the demands of case management and team working.

Part of the enabling role involves empowering the coordinator through offering advice, information, support, and appropriate levels of autonomy. Candidly clarifying the availability of resources so that the coordinator can in turn share the situation with the team is an important part of this process. In order to problem-solve on issues of resource shortfalls for both users and the team as a whole, the team should be given all the information available. Taking this approach with the EIS provided the opportunity for the team to solve the problem of finding an appropriate base away from a hospital site. This produced some innovative solutions and a positive outcome. However, providing the opportunity for problem-solving should not become a licence for devolving responsibility for difficult management decisions to team level or simply failing to manage at all.

Enabling teams also means acting as a buffer against forces which might marginalize the service, particularly at early stages of its development. The EIS attracted considerable hostility from local service providers who felt threatened by a sudden new arrival whose very presence could be interpreted as a criticism of their current practice. In common with the Bridge Programme in Chicago (Witheridge and Dincin, 1985), concern was encountered among other providers over the possibility of the EIS interfering with existing therapeutic relationships or poaching customers for their services. Public sector providers tended to be passionately defensive of their perceived territory while simultaneously at near breaking point with the strain of overwork and interminable waiting lists. The coordinator and the general manager were able to shoulder these reactions jointly, enabling more constructive responses. General management's nurturing role may also take the form of providing guidance and positive strokes for any goals achieved and supporting the coordinator in establishing realistic boundaries for hours worked and case loads within the team. However, perhaps most importantly, general management remains the final back-stop for resolving conflicts between team and professional line management objectives.

Finally, purchasers may also need to take a nurturing role. New services may need to be initially protected against the effects of competition within the provider system by committing continuous funding until they become fully established. For example, the Holyoke/Chicopee service specifically seeded new provider agencies with known good quality personnel and then fostered them until they were self-sustaining. Contracting arrangements for a locality should safeguard the user against discontinuities arising from organizations coming and going according to the vagaries of the market-place.

CONCLUSION

This and the previous chapter have presented a method for structuring and operating teams that aims to achieve the best balance of autonomy against management for both direct-care staff and teams as a whole. This requires clear rather than autocratic leadership at both coordinator and general manager level, and a high level of communication up and down hierarchies. It should be noted that the case management principles of devolved responsibility, accessibility, personal contact, a focus on strengths and needs, and candid communication on the availability of resources also represent good service management practice.

Chapter 11

Service development for high quality

QUALITY ASSURANCE AND CASE MANAGEMENT

The practice of case management itself will not achieve high quality services without the support of a framework for quality assurance. Quality assurance has unfortunately acquired a mysterious and exclusive aura, associated with dark-suited technocrats with expert knowledge and little contact with the daily reality of work with users. This chapter assumes a very simple definition of quality: a high-quality service is one that makes the best possible use of resources to achieve the best possible outcomes for service users. Case management is itself a cyclical process for ensuring positive outcomes for service users and the same approach to quality assurance can be applied at higher levels in the organization.

Quality assurance can be thought of as the whole process for achieving high-quality services or, more narrowly, as the information needed to support this process. The following discussion takes the former approach and views quality assurance in terms of the core tasks of case management: assessment, planning, implementation, monitoring and review.

Assessment

Case management starts by asking an individual service user about their needs. These questions should also be asked of all the users of a provider agency at any given time, and of all the residents of their locality. Table 11.1 describes some of the information needed to stimulate action directed at achieving positive outcomes at each of these three levels (practice level, service provider level, locality/purchaser level). Figure 11.1 (a development of Figure 1.3) illustrates some of the means to achieving this information.

Table 11.1 Levels of activity and information needs

Level and question	Information needs	Action for better outcomes
Purchaser/locality How can the needs of the residents of this locality be better served?	Needs of those already being served. Evaluation of service provision regarding outcome and activity goals tested against agreed standards. Needs of those not being served. Description of people not fulfilling criteria for service provision via case management. Training needs across contracted services.	Support for innovation. Contract development. Issuing of requests for proposals and new contracting. Implementation/ development of training strategy. Ongoing training. Continuing assessment of needs within locality.
Service provider/team How can the needs of this service/team's client group be better served?	Aggregated individual service plans (outcome goal achievement). Feedback from user/ carer groups, Quality Action Groups and other important stakeholders. Criteria for testing adequacy of provision. Training needs (possibly including needs of managers and local service providers). Extent of activity goal achievement.	Changes in practice or management (e.g new eligibility criteria). Continued support for user/carer feedback mechanisms. Implementation/ development of training strategy. Ongoing training.
Case manager – user How can the needs of this particular user be better served?	Individual service plan which highlights areas of met and unmet need. This may include information from an advocate. Personal knowledge, skills and experience needed on the part of case managers, their managers and local service providers.	Changes in practice. Access to new resources. Ongoing training.

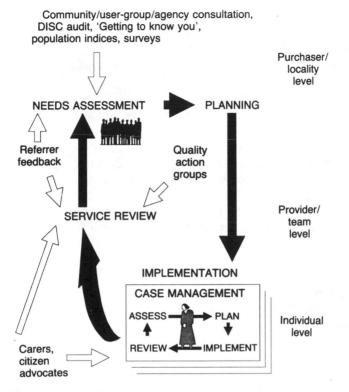

Community/user-group/agency consultation,
DISC audit, 'Getting to know you',
population indices, surveys

Purchaser/
locality
level

NEEDS ASSESSMENT   PLANNING

Referrer
feedback

Quality
action
groups

SERVICE REVIEW

Provider/
team
level

IMPLEMENTATION

CASE MANAGEMENT

ASSESS ──► PLAN

REVIEW ◄── IMPLEMENT

Individual
level

Carers,
citizen
advocates

Figure 11.1 Levels of planning and needs assessment.

Planning

On the basis of this assessment, the organization must decide
upon appropriate outcomes to pursue, and approaches to
achieving them. At practice level these are embodied in the
individual service plan. At provider level they are the outcome
and activity goals within the service's operational policy. At
purchaser level the goals would be enshrined within contracts made with provider agencies. These in turn would be
influenced by objectives contained within health and local
authority community care plans. Smith and Mansell (1991)
recommended that contracts include specific performance
indicators that highlight the achievement of outcomes. For

example, indicators of meaningful and stable vocational place-ments would include feedback from user surveys and the longevity of job placements.

Implementation

Having decided appropriate outcomes and approaches the next challenge is implementation. This is the difficult task of bring-ing about change at different levels within the organization in order that it can adapt to changing demands to achieve the best possible outcomes. This requires continuous innovation. Innovation is any new activity aimed at the achievement of improved outcomes; 'the intentional introduction and applica-tion within a role, group or organization of ideas, processes, products or procedures, new to the relevant unit of adoption, designed to significantly benefit the individual, the group, organization or wider society' (West and Farr, 1989). Training is one example of this activity and achieves positive outcomes by equipping people with the most relevant values, knowledge and skills for the tasks in hand.

Monitoring

A critical feature of effective organizations is their capacity to operate in a learning mode (Beckhard and Harris, 1987). This requires that feedback mechanisms are built into the function-ing of the organization at all levels. In practice many of the methods used for monitoring at each level will be identical to those used for assessment. Both should use users and carers as their principle sources of information. Indeed, as far as poss-ible, assessment and monitoring should be part of the same continuous process.

Review

Reviewing outcomes requires an evaluative judgement on the part of key stakeholders. A crucial question concerns who the key stakeholders are. Harrod (1986) argued that much of the confusion over the definition of appropriate case management practice arises from the failure to differentiate the demands of purchasers, providers, carers and service users. What constitutes high quality depends upon your standpoint. As a user I may consider a high-quality service as one that offers me something meaningful to do during the day. As a worker within a provider agency I may consider quality to be more concerned with the generosity of my travel allowances. Services do not inevitably put the needs of users first and this highlights the need for the organization to adopt and adhere to a clear statement of purpose (or 'mission') that places meeting the needs of users at the top of its agenda. In order to achieve this, service users should be directly involved in the evaluation of services.

USING INFORMATION

The amount of information to be managed within a quality assurance process is immense. Every stakeholder has a view on the past, present and future state of the service, and each activity at every level of the organization demands and generates its own information. Many off-the-shelf approaches to quality assurance provide expert solutions to the task of selecting and assimilating information. The danger is that important (and perhaps discomforting) information is lost on the way. Smith and Mansell (1991) suggested that failure to implement adequate quality assurance systems follows from the naive pursuit of single encompassing measures of quality, and a tendency to emphasize activity goals (e.g. 'The service will achieve vocational placements for 40 users per year') at the expense of outcome goals (e.g. 'The service will achieve meaningful and stable employment for users'). The latter are more difficult to determine yet provide the critical indicators of quality.

If clear responsibility for collecting, collating and reporting information can be established, its sheer volume may begin to look less daunting. This requires that the organization can communicate information up and down hierarchies, and achieve a high-level commitment to making use of relevant information in a planning process.

Needs assessment and monitoring

Figure 11.1 illustrates the variety of sources of information on need within a locality. This includes top-down approaches described in the *Working for Patients* white paper (Cm 555, 1989) whereby Departments of Public Health are responsible for assessing need through surveys and censuses. However, these approaches must be supplemented by qualitative methods for achieving good quality information. The following describes sources that can be used in the continuous process of assessment and monitoring.

Individual service planning

The practice of case management provides the major source of information on the met and unmet needs of people already in contact with the service. Individual service plans should therefore be designed to record desired outcomes and the extent to which these are accomplished. Information from individual service plans can then be aggregated into a statement of the extent to which the service as a whole is meeting the needs of users (Figure and Table 11.1, pp. 208 and 209).

User and carer feedback

If, through a collaborative approach to case management practice, the service is able to maximize the involvement of users and carers in the individual planning process, then this activity itself is a form of user and carer involvement. This is particularly the case if the collaborative approach is safeguarded through the involvement of independent advocates whose views are sought in evaluating the performance of the service. Individual service planning can also be supplemented by interviews collecting feedback on aspects of the service (such as the service questionnaire used by the EIS). However, where the case management model used stresses the importance of a relationship between user and case manager, it is naive to assume that users will be able to offer frank feedback. Other mechanisms are required in addition.

In order to promote frank feedback, user surveys need to be

confidential and explicitly conducted by and for the purchasing agency. Lynch and Kruzich (1986) sampled user views using confidential groups and a structured problem-solving format that excluded staff. Another approach uses structured 'Getting to know you' exercises to assess need by spending considerable time with individual users to develop a full picture of their needs and preferences (Brost and Johnson, 1982). When looking at the outcome of service provision, Smith and Mansell (1991) recommend accessible and user-friendly complaints procedures, along with 'conscience registers' whereby a system is established for people (including workers) involved with services to anonymously 'blow the whistle' on any occurrence of abuse or malpractice.

User and carer groups

Although they vary in style, user groups generally facilitate the involvement of service users in the design and development of services. This format is problematic for a service which has a totally individual focus and works with people in non-institutional environments. People involved in a user group concerned with residential, day or hospital care have the shared experience of a social and physical environment from which to voice their concerns and offer mutual support. The usual experience of a user working with a case manager is that of a relationship with one or two workers. The idea of joining with others who have similar relationships with other case managers may have little perceived relevance.

It can be argued that by concentrating on individually-based approaches to tailoring assistance, case management disempowers users by preventing them coming together with people who share their concerns. The counter-argument is that massing devalued people together with other devalued people is itself disempowering (Brown and Smith, 1991). A crucial consideration in this debate is the power of users to choose. This requires that opportunities exist to use groups to voice concerns, and that other ways of communicating dissent are also available.

Power is a recurrent theme in discussions of user involvement and to avoid tokenism, users involved in service development must operate from a position of influence that is at least equal to other interested parties. When considering a user group for the EIS, team members expressed concern over methods for nominating users to positions of power and their legitimacy to represent the interests of other, perhaps less vocal users. It was noted, however, that other stakeholders were invited to assume power (e.g. through becoming part of the steering group) with little concern over their selection or their legitimacy to advocate on behalf of the people they were claiming to represent. Indeed, given the diversity of people who use services it may be unrealistic to expect users to represent the views of anyone but themselves as individuals. This is nonetheless invaluable information.

As there was no apparent demand for a group connected to the EIS, team members instead worked with motivated users to promote the development of groups that could adopt a locality-wide focus. This would encompass services that users access via case management. However, a major disadvantage of this approach is the lack of connection to anyone purchasing or providing agency to ensure that information will be used.

Quality Action Groups

The Quality in Action Project at the Norah Fry Research Centre (Quality in Action Project, 1991) have developed a quality assurance process through regular group meetings at provider level. The groups always include service users (sometimes with the assistance of people fulfilling an enabling role), and they examine and attempt to improve the performance of the service from the user's perspective. Criteria for quality are based upon outcomes for people who use the service. The groups also involve direct-care staff with the aim of raising their involvement in evaluating and improving the service they provide. The process of Quality Action Groups (QAGs; Figure 11.2) is led by a group leader. All relevant stakeholders are brought together to establish agreed criteria for accomplishment. They then assess the current performance of the service, determine priorities for change, and decide and implement a plan of action. At the end of each cycle the group again reviews the performance of the service and the process is repeated.

QAGs rely heavily on exercises and examples, and leaders are equipped with step-by-step guidance and materials for running the groups.

In order to operate effectively, QAGs require the agreement and active support of senior managers. A coordinator has the job of ensuring that senior management is continuously informed of the work of the groups, supporting the group leaders, and developing and overseeing the QAGs.

QAGs have been concerned with services for people with learning difficulties. However, the approach may also have considerable application with people with severe and long-term mental health problems. Within coordinated teams it

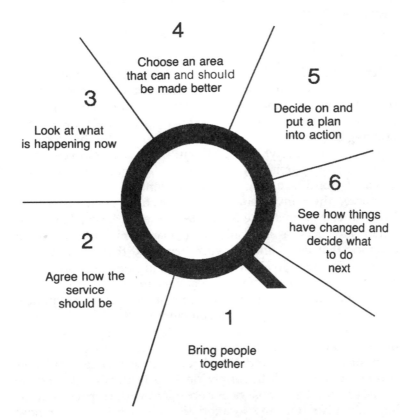

Figure 11.2 Six steps to quality action.

may be appropriate for the team coordinator to assume the group leader function with QAG coordinators employed by purchasers to promote the development of QAGs among provider agencies. Indeed QAGs could usefully become a precondition of the agreement of contracts.

When used in relation to case management teams it is likely that the areas of concern to group members will extent beyond the case management service itself to those agencies that users have linked with. Although this information is relevant to the way the case management service works, it is important that the groups do not become therapy groups concerned with the ways users link up with other agencies.

Citizen advocacy

Citizen advocacy is where 'a valued citizen who is unpaid and independent of human services creates a relationship with a person who is at risk of social exclusion and chooses one or several ways to understand, respond to, and represent that person's interests as if they were the advocate's own, thus bringing that person's gifts and concerns into the circle of ordinary community life' (O'Brien, 1987). As employees of providing or purchasing agencies, case managers are disqualified from assuming an independent advocate role. Furthermore, their involvement in establishing such services is likely to compromise the advocates' independence. However, where advocacy is available, case managers have a role in ensuring that users link up with them, and that advocates are involved in the individual service planning process. Advocates are ideally placed to offer feedback on behalf of users and it is vital that this information contributes to quality assurance. In 1989 there were about a dozen citizen advocacy schemes in Britain following more than 200 well-established schemes in the US, Canada and Australia (Butler and Forrest, 1990). As both share a wholly individual focus, case management and citizen advocacy will hopefully develop in parallel. However, the advocates' base must be independent with respect to funding, administration and location (*ibid.*) and it is unclear how this will be resourced.

Feedback from local providers

As people who refer individuals to a service and observe the outcome, referrers provide a good testing ground for evaluating the achievement of outcome and activity goals. The EIS survey of referrers asked them to indicate their level of agreement with statements relating to outcome (e.g. 'People referred to the service are dissatisfied with the result') and activity (e.g. 'The service is easy to refer to'). In many circumstances, however, it may be more appropriate for purchasers to undertake such surveys in order to achieve more reliable feedback.

Services should also be informed by feedback from other providers who may not have referred but nonetheless have felt the impact of the service's activities. They may be able to highlight areas of unmet need or duplication of effort. Joint working at all levels of the organizations involved will promote the collection and use of such information.

ACHIEVING POSITIVE CHANGE THROUGH INNOVATION

Natural systems are a popular metaphor for understanding the ways in which organizations operate. Many of us talk rather glibly about having a systematic approach to our work but it can be difficult to pin down what this means in practice. Natural systems are awesomely complex and paradoxical; constantly changing while staying confoundedly the same. In order to grapple with this paradox it is necessary to understand the difference between first and second order change (Watzlawick *et al.*, 1974).

Systems resist change in order to maintain a state of balance or homoeostasis. First order change is change that maintains homoeostasis. Individuals aiming to assault this tendency towards inertia within organizations with new ideologies or technologies are apt to find themselves defeated. As Georgiades and Phillimore (1975) stated in their famous account of strategies for organizational change, 'the fact of the matter is that organizations . . . like dragons, eat hero-innovators for breakfast' (p. 315). Innovation is the achievement of second order change; a shift in the organization to a new homoeostasis that produces improved outcomes. Agents of second order change need to be equipped with intelligent strategies and realistic expectations if they are to achieve anything.

Continued failure to innovate on the basis of new information produces organizations that are stuck in patterns that fail to serve both those that are supposed to benefit from its output, and those working within it. As organizations stagnate they lose sight of their aims, potential innovators move on taking their ideas with them, less attention is paid to the most effective use of resources, standards decline and service users suffer.

Characteristics of effective organizations

Innovation is informed by a model of what effective organizations look like. A review of the literature concluded that innovation is associated with 'clear organizational goals and vision; alignment of individuals at all levels of the organization around these goals and vision; an organizational environment which is empowering, where people find good opportunities for growth, and where they are involved in developing and managing the organization; an egalitarian culture which manifests a concern for human growth and is visibly pro-innovation; accountability for results; delegation and decentralization and stress on performance' (West and Farr, 1989, p. 22).

Clear goals and vision

Gaining feedback on innovations is only useful if there is a standard against which results can be judged. These standards are based upon values and beliefs about what a service should be achieving for people, such as the much quoted 'five accomplishments' (O'Brien and Lyle, 1988). The standards and a clear set of priorities for what the organization does and for whom are embodied within the service's overall aims (or 'mission') statement. These aims should also be continuously informed by the quality assurance process described above.

Alignment of individuals at all levels

One of the factors that contribute to organizations becoming purposeless and ineffective is the absence of shared investment in a set of aims amongst all the parties involved. Involving a broad cross-section of stakeholders when developing and revising the aims of the service helps to increase the relevance and longevity of goals set and distributes power throughout the system. However, this dispersal of power must be balanced against the need to maintain the energy of a group of people that is small enough to maintain vision while coping with conflicting demands or hostility. This energy is often described as the 'critical mass' needed for the group to become self-sustaining, self-motivating and cohesive enough to survive the long haul that introducing change usually represents.

Empowering environments

Success is associated with organizational environments where people find good opportunities for growth, and where they are involved in developing and managing the service. This is far from typical, particularly for lower status workers for whom the primary rule may be 'Don't question the rules' and for whom the status quo is 'to maintain the status quo' (Prail and Baldwin, 1988).

An egalitarian culture concerned with personal growth and promoting innovation is needed. Often egalitarian and democratic approaches to team work can be more apparent than real. Lang (1982) described a team with a convivial working atmosphere that professed to be non-hierarchical but that nonetheless consistently allocated the most menial and burdensome tasks to nurses. If egalitarianism and democratic decision-making is to be tenable the structure of work and rewards should serve to maintain these values. Open communication and the expression of differences of opinion on goals, solutions and methods should be rewarded, regardless of the authority relationship between participants. Successful organizations minimize inappropriate competition, and collaboration towards shared aims is rewarded (West and Farr, 1989). Conflict is managed, not suppressed or avoided, and

responsibility for managing conflict is seen as part of everybody's job rather than located with particular managers acting
as referee or arbiter.

Focus on outcomes

Rather than just looking at measures that are presumed to
reflect good practice, such as neat record-keeping or a well-
written aims statement, the organization must focus on outcomes for people that use the service. This demands clear
responsibility for the results achieved, and rewards related to
tasks performed rather than status. Responsibility for outcomes
also means taking responsibility for failure. This is crucial to
the adoption of a learning mode for organizational development since often more is learnt from failure than from success.

Stress on performance

The way work is organized, resources allocated and decisions
made should be shaped by the demands of the tasks involved
rather than the influence of centralized authority or power.
Beckhard and Harris (1987) describe this as 'form following
function'. Decisions made on the basis of information rather
than status provide a way for power to be effectively dispersed
throughout the system.

Delegation and decentralization

Innovation requires that individual workers are empowered to
materially influence their work and their environment. This in
turn relies upon democratic, participative and collaborative
leadership styles within the organization (West and Farr, 1990).

Agents of change

Achieving innovation within a system requires some new input
into it. As with our own personal networks of relationships
between relatives, friends, spouses and lovers, it is often too
difficult to be objective about what is going on when deeply
enmeshed within it. Some external source of energy and infor-

mation is needed to give the system the kind of kick it needs to achieve second order change.

The following are some examples of potential system jolters:

Crisis

If suddenly a feature of the environment in which the organization operates changes, the whole system can be thrown into a crisis where its resources are no longer adequate for the demands being made of it. Loss of funding or the Government rapidly pushing through radical changes in social policy are examples. Perceived competition provides another threat. It is noteworthy that demonstration projects, such as the EIS, can cause great concern to local service providers, not least because central funding means the service comes into operation very rapidly. This may result in hostility and existing service providers suddenly finding the energy to adapt their practice in such a fashion as to squeeze out the unwelcome newcomer.

The boss

The head of the organization may personally assume the task of coordinating change. However, their impact is often impaired through the limited new information that they can bring to problem-solving efforts and they may rely on heavy-handed power tactics to enforce change. Any effects are liable to be marginal or short-lived as those involved in implementing change will have little investment in the process or the outcome. Often the top manager is informed by a 'kitchen cabinet' of cronies selected on the basis of personal trust and their strategic positions within the system. This option is sometimes used where the boss is concerned to maintain overall control of the change process (and perhaps any credit that goes with it) and so the benefits of devolved responsibility and autonomy are unlikely to be reaped.

Hero-innovators

This approach places responsibility for achieving change with individuals who have been sent off to pick up certain skills or knowledge that they then bring back and implement within the organization. Georgiades and Phillimore (1975) criticize the notion that systems can be changed by changing the individuals within it. This 'myth of the hero-innovator' neglects the inter-relationships of individuals within systems, their perceived or actual roles and the tendency of systems to resist change. Georgiades and Phillimore stress the need to prepare the host system for the introduction of any changes that newly trained 'hero-innovators' might try to introduce.

Projects

A popular approach to innovation is to introduce change as an experimental project in some part of the system. This has the significant advantage of allowing any innovation to be piloted on an experimental basis in order to observe the outcomes and iron out unexpected problems. However, there is a danger of projects being used cynically as a way of creating the impression of innovation while doing nothing to effect change in the mainstream. Projects can be set up with inadequate resources and allowed to fail, thereby confirming the pessimistic prognostications of the more reactionary elements within the system. Project members bear the burden of being under scrutiny and must be safeguarded against attempts to evaluate change prematurely.

Groups

Locating responsibility for achieving change with a self-sustaining group of people may offer the best option. Beckhard and Harris (1987) suggest possible candidates for groups to generate the critical mass referred to above. They include:

1. representatives of different groups concerned with the outcome of change. This should include users and carers;
2. members of the hierarchy. Here various line managers are given extra responsibility for aspects of change;
3. 'natural' leaders. These people may not hold formalized authority yet command respect from significant and influential interest groups;
4. a 'diagonal slice' of people concerned with the various functions, tasks and locations involved in the proposed innovation. They need not be of equal formal authority.

Teams as agents of change

Existing teams have a logical advantage in innovation in that they normally already share some sense of vision and common experience and so are well placed to form the core of a critical mass. There are the obvious advantages of pooled ideas, knowledge and experience, and the capacity to protect individual hero-innovators from becoming undermined through isolation and lack of support.

Teams are open systems pulled around by the complex environment in which they are embedded. Their survival, like a skyscraper in a hurricane, depends on the ability to bend without collapsing under the pressure. Teams, as change agents within organizations, need to be able to adapt to shifting patterns and intensity in demands while retaining a clear vision of the aims of the organization. On the basis of their review of the literature on innovation within groups, West and Farr (1990) formulated the model shown in Figure 11.3. The model separates the conditions that determine the quality and the quantity of innovations. Unsurprisingly, many of them parallel the conditions that predict effective organizations generally. Again a *vision* which is clear, negotiated, shared, evolving, valued and attainable assumes central importance in influencing the quality of changes in practice and outcome. This is bolstered by a *climate for excellence* within the team. The expectation of high standards invokes constructive controversy surrounding the quality of tasks for achieving shared goals, and existing practices are appraised and challenged. Also team members check the quality of their ideas before floating them with the group. This tendency is moderated by the effect of *participative safety*. In order to make the social environment of the team safe enough to allow frequent efforts towards innovation, communication should be non-judgemental. If team members feel they can float an idea with the group and receive a considered response, members achieve influence, higher levels of interaction and more sharing of information. This is promoted through democratic, collaborative and participative leadership styles. The attendant devolution of decision-making promotes innovation through increased autonomy and commitment to the tasks at hand. The other major factor determining the quantity of innovation efforts is the *norms for innovation*; the team's expectation, approval and support of attempts to introduce new and improved ways of doing things. This support may take the form of verbal approval or offers of cooperation, time and resources. The values of the elite in any organization powerfully influence the norms for innovation.

Groups of change agents will often benefit from one member taking on the task of coordinating and overseeing the process. Beckhard and Harris (1987) state that 'Managing [complex change] involves a strong ability to deal with ambiguity, a talent for managing conflicts, a deep concern for people and their potential, the ability to maintain a balance between reliance on systematic planning skills and gut feeling, and – most important – having a sense of vision' (p. 116). These qualities are invaluable to the tasks of team coordination (described in Chapter 10) as team coordinators have a central role in ensuring high-quality services at team level.

Building support

Change agents need to recognize the limits of their authority and power at every stage so that they can build upon

Figure 11.3 West's theory of group innovation.

existing influence without over-reaching themselves. Thus, as Georgiades and Phillimore (1975) recommend, it may be necessary to work with those forces within the organization that are most able and willing to change, while avoiding parts that are stuck or malfunctioning, perhaps due to lack of basic resources or deeply held ideologies. Balanced against the merits of working solely with healthy parts of the system is the effect of modelling innovation in parts of the system that are widely regarded as most stuck. For example, in establishing the EIS, the team gained considerable credibility among local providers by specifically targeting the people who the existing system was having most difficulty working with.

It is tempting to go straight to the most senior managers when seeking support for change. However, Georgiades and Phillimore (1975) suggest that individuals at the top level of the organization will often be too identified with the status quo to be adequately motivated towards change, and recommend seeking support among the ranks just below the top. It is also important to seek the support of people who are suffering because of current conditions, and the direct-care staff who would be involved in implementing changes.

Presenting key aspects of the developing operational policy to various interested parties (such as family doctors and other local providers) was the main vehicle for building support for the development of the EIS. This involved a considerable investment in visiting and presentation at meetings.

Managing resistance to change

Resistance to second order change may take many forms and it is important to recognize it and maintain an objective and comparatively dispassionate view. Resistance is normal and inevitable. It is important to keep in mind that those placing obstacles in the path of change may do so for heartfelt and legitimate reasons. It is too easy to become overly cynical, imputing the worst motives.

However, in many cases resistance is fuelled by fear of change *per se* or a desire to maintain the status quo whatever the consequences for users. Prail and Baldwin (1988) have recorded 'Some golden rules for no change (but stay looking good anyway)' employed by reactionaries. They include establishing spurious evaluation procedures employing meaningless measures such as the staff's standard of dress or the amount written in clinical notes; invoking masses of jargon (government policy guidance is an excellent source); sending staff away to train in 'self-awareness' and 'attitude change' while simultaneously discouraging both and ensuring that the effect of training is never evaluated; and above all, procrastination. This last seems particularly to typify the development of demonstration projects and can be recognized through assertions such as, 'We are doing it already', 'We tried it and it didn't work', 'They won't give us the money', 'We will start when we are certain everything is ready' and 'It's not as simple as that'.

The aim in overcoming resistance is to achieve a neutral state where resistance is not being confronted directly but the problem is being clarified. Beckhard and Harris (1987) recommend meeting with opponents to change, and the use of an explicit, collaborative problem-finding approach and minimal structure. Such temporary working groups would be wholly concerned with clarifying the issues and would be prohibited from progressing into taking action. Candour is promoted through avoiding public output in terms of minutes or a public statement of agreement. People need to be helped to listen to each other and change their minds without losing face.

Other ways of overcoming resistance include educational interventions to change attitudes, role modelling of new behaviours and attitudes by key people, and the manipulation of contingencies so that change is rewarded. If the system only rewards concrete results according to a predetermined strategy, innovation would not be anticipated. Reward for innovation must therefore be built into the organization.

ACHIEVING POSITIVE CHANGE THROUGH TRAINING

Training is a central part of a continuous process of innovation based upon information on the needs of service users. It is the process through which people are equipped to deliver the most relevant service, whatever their level in the organization. Since training aims to supply the competences demanded by continuous service development, it must be an ongoing process at every level of the organization rather than a 'hit and run' affair. The training of case managers is therefore as unique as the case management system itself.

The practice of case management will rarely be wholly new to the staff group in question. More usually, case management involves developing existing good practice in order to achieve a more systematic approach that can be evaluated and further built upon. For this reason it is crucial that trainers and innovators acknowledge and use the knowledge, skills and experience of those already working in the field.

A process for identifying competences for case management

The following describes the early stages of work with direct-care staff and their managers on the development of case management. It assumes that case management is to be developed within existing resources, and draws upon the experience of direct-care staff. The intended outcome is a definition of (a) the service developments required in order for the existing service to achieve key indicators of high-quality case management and (b) the competences needed to bring these developments about. The approach could be adapted to achieve any performance indicators defined though a quality assurance process.

Starting off

Often the starting point for the development of case management is a decision by senior managers that an existing team should adopt case management practice. Wherever the initiative arises, senior managers need to make some fundamental decisions about who is to practise case management and for which users. If operating as a team, the type of team and management arrangements must be clarified. From this basis direct-care staff, their line managers and personnel concerned with continuing training can form a working group to develop case management practice. If possible, interested service users should also be involved. The process will need to be led, preferably by someone who will not be directly involved in the emerging service themselves (e.g. one of the training personnel).

Clarifying the remit

Once constituted, the working group needs to have an appreciation of the practical constraints on change for the foreseeable future. This requires that senior managers meet with them to clarify the service developments that must occur as a result of wider policy or resource changes, any predictable future developments that should be considered, and other practical considerations such as critical user characteristics, catchment areas and particular contracted arrangements with specific agencies.

Clarifying intended outcomes

Members of the working group will normally be clear about its function before joining. However, this should be reiterated by the group leader and any ambiguities ironed out. The working group needs to determine how and to whom it is to report its recommendations, and senior managers need to be able to assure the group that the information they receive will be given due consideration. If they cannot give this assurance, the whole exercise should be reconsidered, perhaps with a reconstituted working group that has more credibility. It will be necessary to determine when the group will report and when senior management will feed back their views so that all parties have contracted for a dialogue from the outset.

Creating a climate for sharing concerns

At an early stage it is important to acknowledge that change is potentially very threatening. Group members need to be given permission to voice their concerns in order that they can inform realistic problem-solving and planning. Otherwise issues are likely to become submerged only to emerge later as low motivation, resistance or sabotage.

Describing the key indicators of high-quality case management

At this point the group members contribute their ideas about what a case management service should achieve for users. The DISC framework (described in Chapter 1) offers a structure for thinking about service functions. This is an opportunity for the group to examine its beliefs and values concerning service provision and should not be rushed.

The following five quality indicators cover the essence of case management practice in most situations. However, particular groups may wish to amend or add indicators according to the specifics of local circumstances.

Accessibility and participation
The service should prioritize the people that it is aiming to serve and make itself maximally accessible at all stages of the case management process. The aim is to promote maximum user and carer participation. This requires consideration of the location of the service, physical access, stigma, ease of access for users and carers, equal opportunities to gain access, cultural sensitivity, the need for outreach, the processes of decision-making and the conduct of meetings.

Continuity
Users and carers need to be able to rely on a single point of access over long periods, and times of crisis or transition (e.g. hospital admission). This demands consideration of keyworking and inter-agency boundary issues.

Breadth of function
The service should address the whole range of needs that users present including those concerned with maintenance, growth and development, and crisis resolution.

Individually-based planning
The key objective of case management is the tailoring of provision to an individually assessed profile of needs and strengths. This requires consideration of assessment (rather than just determining eligibility for services); flexibility through maximizing choice and access to resources; high-quality

communication and information; and regular reviews of outcomes.

Clear responsibility and accountability

In order to prevent individuals falling through cracks in service provision, there must be clarity over the respective responsibilities of case managers and other agencies. It is also important to be clear over accountability for service shortfalls, routes of information for quality assurance, and arrangements for the management of direct-care staff working in teams.

Identifying service strengths and weaknesses

Often the existing service is already achieving some of the indicators of high-quality case management. It is therefore important to identify the existing strengths and weaknesses within the present system. One approach is to split the process of clinical work into stages. For example:

1. identification and referral;
2. assessment;
3. planning;
4. implementation and service delivery; and
5. review.

Sub-groups can consider the present service at different stages in terms of its strengths and weaknesses in achieving each of the five indicators. Table 11.2 indicates some of the questions that might be asked at each stage.

Summarizing the present process from the user's viewpoint

Since each stage of clinical work leads on to the next (including review as the process repeats) there will be considerable overlap in the work of the sub-groups. This will assist in piecing together the work of the groups into a coherent picture of the experience of service users. As groups feed back from referral to review the findings can be summarized on a grid of stages by indicators (as Table 11.2) with a traffic-light colour in each cell indicating the attention required (i.e. green indicates that the indicator is already well fulfilled and is not an area for

Table 11.2 Questions for high-quality case management

	Accessibility and participation	Breadth of functions	Individual planning	Continuity	Responsibility and accountability
Referral/ identification	■ Is the service easy to gain access to? ■ Does it screen out clearly inappropriate referrals early enough? ■ Does it have an appropriate image? ■ Does it assertively reach out to the right individuals?	■ Does the service fulfil an appropriate range of functions and is this reflected in the type and sources of referrals?	■ Are referral criteria adequately specified such that any referrer would be clear about whether or not to refer a particular individual? ■ Is enough information gathered at referral to properly plan assessment?	■ Is referral made to the agency that will perform the assessment and coordinate service delivery? ■ Can a potential case manager be identified at this stage	■ Is it clear who is responsible for assisting users that do not fulfil eligibility criteria?

Table 11.2 Continued

	Accessibility and participation	Breadth of functions	Individual planning	Continuity	Responsibility and accountability
Assessment	■ Do assessments take place in a convenient and accessible location for users? ■ Is it easy for other people involved to gain access (e.g. carers or other workers)? ■ Is effective communication ensured, (e.g. through using interpreters)?	■ Does the overall assessment address the full range of needs and strengths that the user and their carers are presenting? ■ Does the service have access to enough specialized assessment skills?	■ Does the location of assessment, choice of assessors and style of assessment take account of characteristics of the user known at referral? ■ Is enough information gathered during assessment to inform planning?	■ Can others already involved with the user, such as other workers and carers, take part in the assessment? ■ Is assessment an ongoing or one-shot event?	■ Is responsibility for coordinating assessment clearly apportioned? ■ Is responsibility for specialized assessments clearly apportioned? ■ Who is accountable if a full assessment cannot be organized?

Planning	■ How do users and carers become involved in the decision-making concerning their future? ■ Does the process of decision-making allow their views to be heard?	■ Is planning actually based on assessment of needs and strengths?	■ Is planning based upon individually assessed strengths and needs rather than gross judgements of eligibility for services? ■ Is enough information collected and are enough people involved in order to plan realistically? ■ Do workers have access to budgets which might increase the flexibility of the individual service plan.	■ Does planning build on existing supports without increasing burden?	■ What influence does the agency concerned with individual planning have over other providers (e.g. does it have a purchasing role)? ■ Is it clear who is responsible for drawing up an individual service plan?

Table 11.2 Continued

	Accessibility and participation	Breadth of functions	Individual planning	Continuity	Responsibility and accountability
Implementation/ service delivery	■ Are the services provided physically accessible, non-stigmatizing, culturally sensitive and used by people who do not have disabilities?	■ Do the services provided address the full breadth of the needs of users and carers and build upon strengths and assets?	■ Does service delivery reflect the individual tailoring of the plan? ■ Is there maximum choice and flexibility? ■ Are service providers equipped with enough information to perform their role properly?	■ Does service delivery complement or usurp existing supports? ■ Can the user be offered a single person to liaise with over issues concerning the services offered? ■ Is the same person or team always available during crises or periods of transition?	■ Who is accountable if one agency involved in implementing a plan fails to deliver? ■ Is it clear to whom the case manager should report short-falls or obstacles?

| Review | How are users and carers involved in decisions about how well the help provided is fulfilling the user's needs and building on their strengths? | Does the review process query the full range of functions that the service (and other services with which it liaises) should be fulfilling for users? | Is the review based upon the specifics of the plan or gross judgements of outcome? Is enough information available at review for a full evaluation? Do reviews occur frequently enough? Do reviews allow for both fine-tuning and radical reform of the individual service plan. | Is the person to whom a user or carer would address comments on the assistance provided the one that coordinated assessment and service delivery? Is there one person continuously monitoring progress? | Who is responsible for ensuring that outcomes are continuously monitored and regularly reviewed? Are lines of accountability for service shortfalls clearly specified? |

concern, red indicates that the service should stop and give the area an in-depth look, and amber comes somewhere in the middle).

Identifying further information required

In the process of the last two stages it is likely that gaps in the knowledge base of the working group may emerge. These gaps should be clarified and the tasks of gathering further information allocated.

Achieving recommendations for the most pressing indicator

The grid will help prioritize the five indicators according to which demand most urgent attention. One indicator should be selected as most central to improving the service. The group can then work on achieving recommendations for change to improve the whole process in terms of that indicator (e.g. continuity). These recommendations should then be prioritized in order of importance.

Achieving recommendations for the other indicators

Sub-groups can then consider the impact of these recommendations on the service in terms of the other indicators. For example, if a recommendation was that workers should assume keyworker roles in order to improve continuity, what are the implications for breadth of need assessed and lines of accountability for aspects of assessment? The sub-groups achieve recommendations to ensure that particular indicators are not compromised.

Drafting a case management system

At this stage, the groups should be in a position to draft a case management system. This can be tested out by imagining a user progressing through the stages from referral to review in a system derived from the recommendations. At each stage the need for information can be determined in order to inform the development of record-keeping systems.

When reporting the outcome of this process to senior management, it is important that recommendations are prioritized since some will be contingent upon others.

Deriving competences

On the basis of a drafted case management system, the group can now begin to brainstorm the skills, knowledge and experience necessary to perform the tasks described. This assessment of training need should cover not only case managers and other direct-care staff, but also team coordinators, line managers, and general managers. At each organizational level, a grid can be drawn up with those requiring the competences down one side (e.g. different professional groups) and the competences summarized across the top (Brown, 1991). The group can then indicate, using the traffic-light colours, those personnel most in need of training. If vertical red lines predominate then multidisciplinary training is probably appropriate. If clear horizontal red lines emerge then particular disciplines may need to be targeted for training.

The process of training

Clearly, the process of training will depend on the competences to be learnt and the present resources of staff. Case managers will be drawn from a range of professional and non-professional staff whose existing skills must be acknowledged. A process involving self-assessments of training need, a variety of formats and selection of training modules from a menu of available resources may be needed to achieve the necessary flexibility. Supervised learning on the job may provide the core input, and it is crucial that learning relates to real-life experiences, uses local resources, and key local personnel who know the area.

It is fortunate that the creation of new case manager roles coincides with the introduction of a framework for National Vocational Qualifications. This requires clear specification of the demands of the new role and the necessary competences. Using this information, induction and training plans can be drawn up that supply the knowledge and skills required. The framework also requires the nomination of a training facilitator in the workplace who has the job of overseeing training and assisting the trainee in assessing their training needs. This function must link to systems for staff performance appraisal. Watts and Bennett (1983) point out that feedback on performance only increases staff effectiveness where strategies for improvement can be identified, and staff receive appropriate support in adopting and persisting with new practices. The case management team coordinator would therefore be a suitable person to fulfil the role of training facilitator for trainee case managers.

Hoult (1986) provided an example of the training required for a service operating a case management model similar to that described in this book. Workers were professional staff who had no previous experience of case management in a community team. Training consisted mainly of role plays of likely situations to be encountered. A problem-solving approach was used along with formal lectures on medication, the recognition of side effects, and systems and family theories. The team also learnt about the locality and the resources within it. Two or three weeks' training appeared to be adequate for professional staff.

Multidisciplinary training is the logical corollary of a greater emphasis on multidisciplinary working. A team format will be particularly relevant to training aimed at inculcating a shared value-base, pooling knowledge of resources within and outside the team, and team-based procedures concerning, for example, screening at referral and assessment, information systems and the quality assurance process. Mechanic (1986) advocates joint training by schools of nursing and social work for particularly sophisticated practitioners of case management.

Training service users

Case management demands of the worker that they appreciate the difficulties and practical obstacles facing someone with severe and long-term mental health problems. People who have had similar experiences themselves are uniquely qualified to fulfil this role. Arising out of a need for staff, the Denver Citywide Case Management service introduced a programme to train 'consumer case managers' to perform some of the 'paraprofessional' tasks of case management such as outreach, communications between agencies, advocacy with entitlements and provider agencies, counselling and support, and teaching communication and coping skills (Sherman and Porter, 1991). A competence-based approach (as above) to determining training need was derived from task descriptions supplied by programme directors and managers concerned with re-sourcing. A curriculum was designed and job descriptions drawn up on the basis of this information. The successful candidates were selected on the basis of their motivation and ability to overcome deficits. Training was highly individualized and included classroom and supervised on-the-job training. The classroom training included not only case management skills but remedial work (e.g. on reading and arithmetic).

Training and subsequent placement was successful and demand for consumer case managers has subsequently in-creased. Originally, their aim was to train 20 consumer case managers to job-share ten full-time jobs so that the work was covered should individuals experience recurrences of their mental distress. This proved to be unnecessary and the in-ability of employers to fund additional hours of employment became a source of frustration. The authors report increased awareness of the potential of people with severe and long-term mental health problems among providers, and an expansion of user employment into other provider roles.

The future of training

A professional background, and education to Bachelor or Masters level is normally assumed in order to be able to prac-tise case management in the manner described in this book (Maurin, 1990). The American Nurses Association recom-mended in 1988 that the minimum preparation for a nurse case manager was a Bachelor in nursing followed by three years of appropriate clinical experience (*ibid.*). However, another positive corollary of the introduction of National Vocational Qualifications is the potential for improved access to pro-fessional training. Indeed, with a greater emphasis on the competences required to perform the job, the need for a core set of professional skills may break down. Hopefully, this will result in the employment of service users and people with a wider range of backgrounds as case managers.

The impact of case management on professional training will clearly be linked to its effect on professional practice. Case management will have different implications for different professions. For example, it may accelerate a trend within nursing towards greater practice autonomy. For social workers, it may mean a renaissance of traditional field social work values that emphasize the basic material needs of users. The psychologist's skills in service evaluation and behavioural work may come to the fore. Psychiatrists may have to adjust to greater emphasis on work in primary care settings, less reliance on control of hospital beds as their source of decision-making influence, and a more narrowly defined role that emphasizes their particular skills in assessment and psychotropic medication management. Training will need to reflect these changes in both its form and content. For example, as services become decentralized from hospitals and are dispersed to community settings, the institutional ward round will become increasingly irrelevant as a forum for the training of junior medical staff.

The future of training in case management will also inevitably be affected by salary incentives and working environments that promote continuing professional development in work with people with severe and long-term mental health problems. Services for this client group have failed to attract and keep ambitious young workers in the past. Therefore, case management training must include continued support and supervision from experienced and high status case management practitioners (Shepherd, 1990). This also requires a radical shift in the targeting of resources away from acute hospital care to community-based services that place people 'most in need' at the top of their agenda.

LOOKING AHEAD

There will always be a need for mental health service provision in anything other than a utopian world. The extent of a society's investment in resources for its most devalued and distressed citizens is arguably the critical indicator of its civilization. Case management should have a central role in making the best possible use of those resources in order to achieve the best possible outcomes for service users. However, case management is in danger of appearing to be all things to all people; the last in a series of panaceas for the ills of under-funded community care. For this reason, case management services must be very specific about their aims and limitations, and operate within a system that strives for positive outcomes for service users. Within a context of clear agency responsibilities and adequate resources, case management has enormous potential to achieve accessible, continuous, coordinated, flexible and efficient services, and workers may find themselves taking a more holistic and autonomous approach to their work within clearly managed team frameworks. The core tasks of case management, its cyclical nature and emphasis on devolved responsibility, increased autonomy, and empowerment through collaboration and sharing of information, are all features that can be usefully applied to organizations as a whole.

Increased choice and flexibility of provision within non-stigmatizing and supportive environments is needed in order to promote the integration of people with severe and long-term mental health problems into communities. This will only come about through continued advocacy and lobbying which in turn requires that people come together to share and understand the experiences of people in severe mental distress. Case management has been described in this book as an approach that stresses greater personal contact between mental health workers, users and carers. With accessible training for case management and the increased involvement of members of the public in advocacy roles, the mystification and overprofessionalization of mental health work may at last begin to break down. Although resources for people with severe and long-term mental health problems continue to be very inadequate, case management may provide an opportunity for service users, workers and ordinary members of the public to tackle future obstacles together.

References

Accreditation Council for Psychiatric Facilities. (1976) *Principles of Accreditation of Community Mental Health Service Programs.* Joint Commission on Accreditation of Hospitals.

Altman, H. (1983) A collaborative approach to discharge planning for chronic mental patients. *Hospital and Community Psychiatry,* **34,** 641–2.

Anthony, W. A. and Blanch, A. (1989) Research on Community Support Services: what have we learned? *Psychosocial Rehabilitation Journal,* **12** (3), 55–81.

Audit Commission. (1986) *Making a Reality of Community Care.* HMSO, London.

Axelrod, S. and Wetzler, S. (1989) Factors associated with better compliance with psychiatric aftercare. *Hospital and Community Psychiatry,* **40** (4), 397–401.

Bachrach, L. L. (1980) Overview: model programs for chronic mental patients. *American Journal of Psychiatry,* **137** (9), 1023–31.

Baker, R. and Hall, J. N. (1983) *Rehabilitation Evaluation, Hall and Baker (REHAB).* Vine Publishing, Aberdeen.

Baldwin, S., Baser, C. and Harding, K. (1991) *Multi Level Needs Assessment.* British Association for Behavioural Psychotherapy, London.

Beardshaw, V. and Towell, D. (1990) *Assessment and case management: implications for the implementation of 'Caring for People'.* Kings Fund Institute Briefing Paper (10). Kings Fund, London.

Beck, A. T., Ward, C. H., Mendelson, M., Mock, J., Erbaugh, J. et al. (1961) An inventory for measuring depression. *Archives of General Psychiatry,* **4,** 561–71.

Beckhard, R. and Harris, R. T. (1987) *Organizational Transitions: Managing Complex Change* (2nd ed.) Addison-Wesley, Reading, Mass.

Bell, L. (1989) The politics of clinical psychology in adult mental health, *Clinical Psychology Forum,* **20,** 3–5.

Bennett, D. H. (1978) Social forms of psychiatric treatment, in (ed.) J. K. Wing *Schizophrenia: Towards a New Synthesis,* Academic Press, London.

Bentall, R. P. (1990) The syndrome and symptoms of psychosis, in *Reconstructing Schizophrenia* (ed. R. P. Bentall) Routledge, London.

Berzon, P. and Lowenstein, B. (1984) A flexible model of case management. *New Directions for Mental Health Services*, **21**, 49–57.

Blackwell, T. and Jarman, B. (1991) *Lisson Grove Benefits Programme V2.8*. Lisson Grove Health Centre, London.

Blunden, R., Evans, G. and Humphreys. S. (1987) *Planning with Individuals: An Outline Guide*. Mental Handicap in Wales Applied Research Unit, Cardiff.

Bond, G. R., Miller, L. D., Krumweid, R. D. and Ward, R. S. (1988) Assertive case management in three CMHCs: a controlled study. *Hospital and Community Psychiatry*, **39** (4), 411–18.

Borland, A., McRae, J. and Lycan, C. (1989) Outcomes of five years of intensive case management. *Hospital and Community Psychiatry*, **40** (4), 369–76.

Braisby, D., Echlin, R. Hill, S. and Smith, H. (1988) *Changing Futures*. Kings Fund, London.

Brandon, D. and Towe, N. (1989) *Free to Choose: An Introduction to Service Brokerage*. Good Impressions Publishing Ltd, London.

Brewin, C. R., Wing, J. K., Mangen, S. P. *et al.* (1988) Needs for care among the long-term mentally ill: a report from the Camberwell High Contact Survey. *Psychological Medicine*, **18**, 457–68.

British Psychological Society (1986) *Responsibility Issues in Clinical Psychology and Multidisciplinary Teamwork*. Leicester. BPS.

Brost, M. and Johnson, T. (1982) *Getting to Know You: One approach to Service Assessment and Planning for Individuals with Disabilities*. Wisconsin Council on Developmental Disabilities, Madison.

Brown, G. W. and Harris, T. O. (1978) *Social Origins of Depression: A Study of Psychiatric Disorder in Women*. Tavistock, London.

Brown, H. (1991) *New Skills for Old – Training Case Managers* Discussion paper. University of Kent, Canterbury.

Brown, H. and Bassett, T. (1988) *First Things First: A Team Building Manual for Community Mental Handicap and Community Mental Health Teams*. South East Thames Regional Health Authority, Bexhill-on-Sea.

Brown, H. and Smith, H. (1989) Whose ordinary life is it anyway? *Disability, Handicap and Society*, **4**, 105–19.

Brown, H. and Smith, H. (eds.) (1991) *Normalisation: A Reader for the 1990s*. Routledge, London.

Brown, R. and Wade, G. (1987) Superordinate goals and intergroup behaviour: the effect of role ambiguity and status on intergroup attitudes and task performance. *European Journal of Social Psychology*, **17**, 131–42.

Brugha, T. S. (1984) Personal losses and deficiencies in social networks. *Social Psychiatry*, **19**, 69–74.

Brunton, J. and Hawthorne, H. (1989) The acute non-hospital: a California model. *The Psychiatric Hospital*, **20** (2), 95–9.

Butler, K. and Forrest, A. (1990) Citizen advocacy for people with disabilities, in Winn, L. (ed.) *Power to the People: The Key to Responsive Services in Health and Social Care*. King's Fund, London.

Cambridge, P. (1992) Case management, in *Care in the Community: Challenge and demonstration*. eds. Knapp, M., Cambridge, P., Thomason, C., Allen, C., Beecham, J. and Darton, R. Gower, Aldershot.

Campbell, P. (1990) Mental health self-advocacy, in (ed.) L. Winn *Power to the People: The Key to Responsive Services in Health and Social Care*. King's Fund, London.

Caplan, G. (1964) *Principals of Preventive Psychiatry*. Tavistock, London.

Careplan: *Packaging, Purchasing and Managing Care*. NFER-Nelson, Windsor.

Carpenter, J. and Treacher, A. (1989) *Problems and Solutions in Marital and Family Therapy*. Blackwell, Oxford.

Carpenter, W. and Heinrichs, D. (1983) Early intervention, time-limited, targeted pharmacotherapy of schizophrenia. *Schizophrenia Bulletin*, **9**, 553–42.

Carpenter, W. T., Hanlon, T. E., Heinrichs, D. W. *et al.* (1990) Continuous versus targeted medication in schizophrenic out-patients: outcome results. *American Journal of Psychiatry*, **147** (9), 1138–48.

Caton, C. L. M. (1981) The new chronic patient and the system of community care. *Hospital and Community Psychiatry*, **7**, 475–8.

Challis, D. J. (1990) Case management: problems and possibilities, in *Care Managers and Care Management* (ed.), T. Allen. Policy Studies Institute, London.

Challis, D. J. and Davies, B. P. (1986) *Case Management in Community Care*. Gower, Aldershot.

Chamberlin, J., Rogers, J. A. and Sneed, C. C. (1989) Consumers, families and community support systems. *Psychosocial Rehabilitation Journal*, **12** (3), 91–106.

Clifford, P. and Craig, T. (1988) *Case Management Systems for the Long-term Mentally Ill: A Proposed Inter-agency Initiative*. National Unit for Psychiatric Research and Development, London.

Cm 555 (1989) *Working for Patients*. HMSO, London.

Cm 849 (1989) *Caring for People*. HMSO, London.

Cmnd 6233 (1975) *Better Services for the Mentally Ill*. HMSO, London.

Cutler, D. L., Tatum, E. and Shore, J. H. (1987) A comparison of schizophrenic patients in different community support treatment approaches. *Community Mental Health Journal*, **23**, 103–13.

Davis, A. (1990) A constructive escape route – who wants day care? in

Day Care Information Pack. (ed. R. Echlin) Good Practices in Mental Health, London.

Department of Health (1990) *Community Care in the Next Decade and Beyond*. HMSO, London.

Department of Health and Social Security (1980) *Organisational and Management Problems of Mental Illness Hospitals*. HMSO, London.

Deschamps, J. and Brown, R. (1983) Superordinate goals and intergroup conflict. *British Journal of Social Psychology*, **22**, 189–95.

Dill, A. E. P. (1987) Issues in case management for the chronically mentally ill. *New Directions for Mental Health Services*, **36**, 61–70.

Dowell, A. and Ciarlo, J. A. (1983) Overview of community mental health centres program for an evaluation perspective. *Community Mental Health Journal*, **19** (2), 95–125.

Early Intervention Service. (1989) *Annual report*. Available from EIS, Unit 5, 1–31 Elkstone Road, London W10 5NT.

East Anglian Regional Health Authority/Office for Public Management (1990) *Contracting for Health Outcomes*. EARHA/OPM, Cambridge.

Echlin, R. (ed.) (1988) *Community Mental Health Centres/Teams Information Pack*. Good Practices in Mental Health/Interdisciplinary Association of Mental Health Workers, London.

Ellis, R. H., Wilson, N. Z. and Foster, F. M. (1984) Statewide treatment and outcome assessment in Colorado: The Colorado Client Assessment Record (CCAR) *Community Mental Health Journal*, **20**, 72–88.

Fadden, G., Bebbington, P. and Kuipers, L. (1987) The burden of care: the impact of functional psychiatric illness on the patient's family. *British Journal of Psychiatry*, **150**, 285–92.

Fagin, L. and Purser, H. (1986) Development of the Waltham Forest Local Mental Health Case Register. *Bulletin of the Royal College of Psychiatrists*, **10**, 303–6.

Falloon, I. R. H., Boyd, J. L. and McGill, C. W. (1984) *Family Care of Schizophrenia*. Guildford Press, London.

Fariello, D. and Scheidt, S. (1989) Clinical case management of the dually diagnosed patient. *Hospital and Community Psychiatry*, **40**, (10), 1065–7.

Fernando, S. (1988) *Race and Culture in Psychiatry* Tavistock/Routledge, London.

Fischer, P. J. and Breakley, W. R. (1986) Homelessness and mental health: an overview. *International Journal of Mental Health*, **14**, 6–41.

Fisher, G., Landis, G. and Clark, K. (1988) Case management service provision and client change. *Community Mental Health Journal*, **24** (2), 134–42.

Francis, E., David, J., Johnson, N. and Sashidharan, S. P. (1989) Black people and psychiatry in the UK. *Psychiatric Bulletin*, **13**, 482–5.

Franklin, J. L., Solovitz B., Mason, M., Clemons, J. R. and Miller, G. (1987) An evaluation of case management. *American Journal of Public Health*, **77**, 674–8.

Gawlinski, G. and Graessle, L. (1988) *Planning Together: The Art of Effective Teamworking*. Bedford Square Press, London.

Geer, J. H. (1965) The development of a scale to measure fear, *Behaviour Research and Therapy*, **3**, 45–53.

Georgiades, N. J. and Phillimore, L. (1975) The myth of the hero-innovator and alternative strategies for organisation change, in *Behaviour Modification with the Severely Retarded* eds. C. C. Kiernan and E. P. Woodford. Associated Scientific Publishers, Elsevier, North Holland.

Gibson, D. (1989) Requisites for excellence: structure and process in delivering psychiatric care. *Occupational Therapy in Mental Health*, **9** (2), 27–52.

Glennerster, H. Korman, N. and Marslen-Wilson, F. (1983) *Planning for Priority Groups*. Martin Robertson, Oxford.

Goering, P. N., Wasylenki, D. A., Farkas, M., Lancee, W. J. and Ballantyne, R. (1988) What difference does case management make? *Hospital and Community Psychiatry*, **39** (3), 272–6.

Goffman, E. (1961) *Asylums*. Penguin, Harmondsworth.

Goldberg, D. and Huxley, P. (1980) *Mental Illness in the Community*. Tavistock, London.

Goldberg, E. M. and Connelly, N. (1982) *The Effectiveness of Social Care for the Elderly*. Heinemann, London.

Goldfinger, S. M., Hopkins, J. T. and Surber, R. W. (1984) Treatment resisters or system resister? Towards a better service system for acute care recidivists. *New Directions for Mental Health Services*, **21**, 17–27.

Goodwin, S. (1989) Community care for the mentally ill in England and Wales: myths, assumptions and reality. *Journal of Social Policy*, **18** (1), 27–52.

Griffiths, R. (1988) *Community Care: Agenda for Action*. HMSO, London.

Hadley, R. and McGrath, M. (1984) *When Social Services are Local*. Bedford Square Press, London.

Hagan, T. (1990) Accessible and acceptable services, in Huxley, P. *Effective Community Mental Health Services*. Avebury/Gower, Aldershot.

Harris, M. and Bergman, H. (1988) Clinical case management for the chronically mentally ill: a conceptual analysis. *New Directions for Mental Health Services*, **40**, 5–13.

Harrod, J. B. (1986) Defining case management in community support systems. *Psychosocial Rehabilitation Journal*, **9** (3), 56–61.

Hatch, S. and Nissel, C. (1989) *Survey of Psychiatric Patients Discharged into Westminster*. Westminster Association for Mental Health, London.

Henderson, A. S. (1984) Interpreting the evidence on social support. *Social Psychiatry*, **19**, 49–52.

Hersen, M. and Bellack, A. S. (eds.) (1976) *Behavioral Assessment: A Practical Handbook*. Pergamon Press, New York.

Hollander, E. P. (1978) *Leadership Dynamics: A Practical Guide to Effective Relationships*. Free Press, New York.

Holloway, F. (1991) Case management for the mentally ill: looking at the evidence. *International Journal of Social Psychiatry*, **37** (1), 2–13.

Hospital and Community Psychiatry, (1986) Gold award: A network of services for the homeless chronic mentally ill. **37** (11), 1149–51.

Hoult, J. (1986) Community care of the acutely mentally ill. *British Journal of Psychiatry*, **149**, 137–44.

House of Commons Social Services Committee (1985) *Second Report on 'Community Care with Special Reference to Adult Mentally Ill and Mentally Handicapped People'*. (HC 13 1984–85). HMSO, London.

House of Commons Social Services Committee (1990a) *Eighth Report on 'Community Care: Planning and Co-operation'*. (HC 580-I). HMSO, London.

House of Commons Social Services Committee (1990b) *Eleventh Report on 'Community Care: Services for People with a Mental Handicap and People with a Mental Illness'*. HMSO, London.

Hudson, B. (1987) Steering a course through the myths of community care. *Health Service Journal*, 27th June, Centre 8.

Huxley, P. (1990) *Effective Community Mental Health Services*. Avebury/Gower, Aldershot.

Intagliata, J. (1982) Improving the quality of care for the chronically mentally disabled: the role of case management. *Schizophrenia Bulletin*, **8** (4), 655–73.

Intagliata, J., Barry, W. and Egri, G. (1988) The role of the family in delivering case management services. *New Directions for Mental Health Services*, **40**, 39–50.

Jabitsky, I. M. (1988) Psychiatric teams and the psychiatrist's authority in the New York State mental health system. *New York State Journal of Medicine*, **88** (11), 577–81.

Kanter, J. (1985) Case management of the young adult chronic patient: a clinical perspective. *New Directions for Mental Health Services*, **27**, 77–92.

Kanter, J. (1989) Clinical case management: definition, principles, components. *Hospital and Community Psychiatry*, **40** (4), 361–8.

Kiesler, C. A. (1982) Mental hospitals and alternative care. *American Psychologist*, **37**, 349–60.

King, R., Raynes, N. and Tizard, J. (1971) *Patterns of Residential Care*.

Routledge and Kegan Paul, London.

Knapp, M., Beecham, J., Anderson, J. *et al.* (1990) The TAPS project: predicting the community costs of closing psychiatric hospitals. *British Journal of Psychiatry*, **157**, 661–70.

Knapp, M., Cambridge, P., Thomason, C. *et al.* (1992) *Care in the Community: Challenge and demonstration.* Gower, Aldershot.

Knoedler, W. (1989) The continuous treatment team model: role of the psychiatrist. *Psychiatric Annals*, **19** (1), 35–40.

Lamb, H. R. (1980) Therapist-case managers: more than just brokers of services. *Hospital and Community Psychiatry*, **31** (11), 762–3.

Lang, C. L. (1982) The resolution of status and ideological conflicts in a community mental health setting. *Psychiatry*, **45**, 159–71.

Leavitt, S. S. (1983) Case management: a remedy for the problems of community care, in *Case Management in Mental Health Services*, (ed. C. J. Sanbourn). Haworth Press, New York.

Leff, J., Kuipers, L., Berkowitz, R. *et al.* (1982) A controlled trial of social intervention in the families of schizophrenic patients. *British Journal of Psychiatry*, **141**, 121–34.

Leff, J., Kuipers, L., Berkowitz, R. and Sturgeon, D. (1985) A controlled trial of social intervention in the families of schizophrenic patients: two year follow-up. *British Journal of Psychiatry*, **146**, 594–600.

Leiter, M. P. (1988) Burnout as a function of communication patterns: a study of a multidisciplinary mental health team. *Group and Organisational Studies*, **13** (1), 11–128.

Levine, I. S. and Fleming, M. (1984) *Human Resource Development Issues in Case Management.* Center for Rehabilitation and Manpower Services. University of Maryland, College Park, MD.

Liberman, R. P., Falloon, I. R. H. and Aitchision, R. A. (1984) Multiple family therapy for schizophrenia. A behavioural problem-solving approach. *Psychosocial Rehabilitation Journal*, **7**, 60–77.

Liberman, R. P., Mueser, K. T., Wallace, C. J. *et al.* (1986) Training skills in the psychiatrically disabled: learning coping and competence. *Schizophrenia Bulletin*, **12**, 631–47.

Lipton, F. R., Cohen, C. I., Fischer, E. and Katz, S. E. (1981) Schizophrenia: a network crisis. *Schizophrenia Bulletin*, **7**, 144–51.

Lynch, M. M. and Kruzich, J. M. (1986) Needs assessment of the chronically mentally ill: practitioner and client perspectives. *Administration in Mental Health*, **13** (4), 237–48.

Masson, J. (1988) *Against Therapy.* London: Fontana.

Maurin, J. T. (1990) Case management: caring for psychiatric patients. *Journal of Psychosocial Nursing*, **28** (7), 8–12.

McRae, J., Higgins, M., Lycan, C. and Sherman, W. (1990) What happens to patients after five years of intensive case management stops? *Hospital and Community Psychiatry*, **41** (2), 175–9.

Mechanic, D. (1986) The challenge of chronic mental illness: a retrospective and prospective view. *Hospital and Community Psychiatry*, **37** (9), 891–6.

Merson, S., Tyrer, P., Onyett, S. R., Lynch, S. and Lack, S. (1991) A controlled evaluation of early intervention in psychiatric emergencies. Unpublished manuscript. Available from Professor P. Tyrer. St Charles Hospital, London, W10 6DZ.

Miller, G. (1983) Case management: the essential service, in *Case Management in Mental Health Services* (ed. C. J. Sanborn). Haworth Press, New York.

Milne, D., Jones, R. and Walters, P. (1989) Anxiety management in the community: a social support model and preliminary evaluation. *Behavioural Psychotherapy*, **17**, 221–36.

MIND/Roehampton Institute (1990) *People First. Special Report*. MIND, London.

Modrcin, M., Rapp, C. A. and Poertner, J. (1988) The evaluation of case management services for the chronically mentally ill. *Evaluation and Program Planning*, **11** (4), 307–14.

Moroney, R. M. (1976) *The Family and The State*. Longman, London.

Morrish, J. (1988) Competence in care. *Insight*, 25 October, 16–18.

Mosher, L. R. (1983) Alternatives to psychiatric hospitalisation: Why has research failed to be translated into practice? *New England Journal of Medicine*, **309**, 25, 1579–80.

Mosher, L. R. and Burti, L. (1989) *Community Mental Health: Principles and Practice*. Norton, New York.

Mueller, B. J. and Hopp, M. (1987) Attitudinal, administrative, legal and fiscal barriers to case management in social rehabilitation of the mentally ill. *International Journal of Mental Health*, **15** (4), 44–58.

Muijen, M. (1990) *Short Term Outcome of a Study Comparing Home Care with Standard Hospital Care*. MSc thesis. London School of Hygiene and Tropical Medicine, London.

Muijen, M., Marks, I. M., Connolly, J. *et al.* (In press) The daily living programme: preliminary comparison of community versus hospital based treatment for the seriously mentally ill facing emergency admission. *British Journal of Psychiatry*.

Mulkern, V. and Spense, R. (1984) *Alcohol abuse/alcoholism among homeless persons: a review of the literature*. National Institute on Alcoholism and Alcohol Abuse, Rockville, MD.

National Institute of Mental Health (1977) *Comprehensive Community Support Systems for Severely Mentally disabled Adults: Definitions, Components, and Guiding Principles*. NIMH, Rockville, MD.

Nuechterlein, K. H. and Dawson, M. E. (1984) A heuristic vulnerability stress model of schizophrenic episodes. *Schizophrenia*

Bulletin, **10**, 300–12.

O'Brien, J. (1987) *Learning from Citizen Advocacy Programs*. Advocacy Office, Georgia, USA.

O'Brien, J. and Lyle, C. (1988) *Framework for Accomplishment*. Responsive Systems Associated. Atlanta, Georgia.

Office of Health Economics (1989) *Mental Health in the 1990s*. Briefing paper no. 90. OHE, London.

Olfson, M. (1990) Assertive community treatment: an evaluation of the experimental evidence. *Hospital and Community Psychiatry*, **41** (6), 634–41.

Onyett, S. R. (1991a) People without homes: a call for psychology. *Clinical Psychology Forum*, **32**, 22–6.

Onyett, S. R. (1991b) An agenda for care programming and care management. *Health Services Management*, **87** (4), 180–3.

Onyett, S. R. (1992) Assertive help for inner city distress, in *Prevention of Anxiety and Depression*. Department of Health Conference Series, **1** (1) HMSO, London.

Onyett, S. R., Tyrer, P., Connolly, J. *et al.* (1990) The Early Intervention Service: the first 18 months of an inner London demonstration project. *Psychiatric Bulletin*, **14**, 267–9.

Ovretveit J. (1986) *Organising Multidisciplinary Community Teams*. BIOSS working paper.

Owens, R. G. and Ashcroft, J. B. (1982) Functional analysis in applied psychology. *British Journal of Clinical Psychology*, **21**, 181–9.

Parker, S. and Knoll, J. L. (1990) Partial hospitalization: an update. *American Journal of Psychiatry*, **147** (2), 156–60.

Patton, M. Q. (1986) *Utilization-focused Evaluation*. Sage, California.

Peck, E. and Smith, H. (1990) *Contracting in Psychiatry*. National Health Service Training Directorate, Bristol.

Pepper, B. and Ryglewicz, H. (1984) Concluding comments. *New Directions for Mental Health Services*, **21**, 110–13.

Pilling, D. (1988) *The Case Manager Project: Report of the Evaluation*. Rehabilitation Resource Centre, Department of Systems Science, City University, London.

Prail, T. and Baldwin, S. (1988) Beyond hero-innovation: real change in unreal systems. *Behavioural Psychotherapy*, **16**, 1–14.

President's Commission on Mental Health (1978) Report of the Task Panel on Deinstitutionalisation, Rehabilitation and Long Term Care. *Task Panel Reports Submitted to the President's Commission on Mental Health*, Vol II, 256–378. Washington DC.

Provencal, G. (1987) Culturing commitment, in Taylor, S. J., Bilen, D. and Knoll, J. *Community Integration for People with Severe Disabilities*. Teachers College Press, New York.

Psychiatric Team for Single Homeless People (1990) *Plugging the Gaps*.

Lewisham and North Southwark Health Authority. Available from the Executive Administrator, Mental Health Service, Doctor's House, Wardalls Grove, London.

Putnam, J. F., Cohen, N. L. and Sullivan, A. M. (1986) Innovative outreach services for the homeless mentally ill. *International Journal of Mental Health*, **14** (4), 112–24.

Quality in Action Project (1991) *Quality in Action: A Resource Pack for Improving Services for People with Learning Difficulties*. Pavilion Publishing, Brighton.

Rachman, S. and Hodgson, R. (1974) Synchrony and desynchrony in fear and avoidance. *Behaviour Research and Therapy*, **12**, 311–18.

Rapp, C. A. and Wintersteen, R. (1989) The strengths model of case management: results from twelve demonstrations. *Psychosocial Rehabilitation Journal*, **13** (1), 23–32.

Renshaw, J., Hampson, R., Thomason, C. *et al.* (1988) *Care in the Community: The First Steps*. Gower, Aldershot.

Rose, S. M., Peabody, C. G. and Stratigeas, B. (1991) Undetected abuse among intensive case management clients. *Hospital and Community Psychiatry*, **42** (5), 499–503.

Rosen, R. (1977) *PsychoBabble*. Wildwood House, London.

Rosenfield, S., Caton, C., Nachumi, G. and Robbins, E. (1986) Closing the gaps: the effectiveness of linking programmes connecting chronic mental patients from the hospital to the community. *Journal of Applied Behavioural Science*, **22** (4), 411–23.

Rosenhan, D. L. (1973) On being sane in insane places. *Science*, **179**, 250–8.

Rowe, D. (1988) Foreword, in J. Masson. *Against Therapy*. Fontana, London.

Royal College of Psychiatrists (1989) *Guidelines for Good Medical Practice in Discharge and Aftercare Procedures for Patients Discharged from an Inpatient Setting*. RCP, London.

Ryan, P., Ford, R. and Clifford, P. (1991) *Case Management and Community Care*. London: Research and Development for Psychiatry.

Ryglewicz, H. (1984) An agenda for family intervention: issues, models and practice. *New Directions for Mental Health Services*, **21**, 81–90.

Satchell, M. (1988) *Health and Homelessness: A Study of Health Problems in Single Homeless Men*. Unpublished MSc dissertation. Polytechnic of the South Bank.

Sayce, L. (1990) *Waiting for Community Care: Implications of Government Policy for 1991*. MIND, London.

Scheff, T. J. (1975) Introduction in *Labelling Madness*. (ed. T. J. Scheff) Prentice-Hall, New Jersey.

Scheff, T. J. (1985) *Being Mentally Ill*. Aldine, New York.

Schlesinger, M., Dorwart, R. A. and Pulice, R. T. (1986) Competitive bidding and states purchase of services: the case of mental health care in Massachusetts. *Journal of Policy Analysis and Management*, **5** (2), 245–63.

Shepherd, G. (1984) *Institutional Care and Rehabilitation*. Longman, Harlow.

Shepherd, G. (1990) Case management. *Health Trends*, **22** (2), 59–61.

Shepherd, G. and Richardson, A. (1979) Organisation and interaction in psychiatric day centres. *Psychological Medicine*, **9**, 573–9.

Sherif, M. (1966). *Group Conflict and Cooperation: Their Social Psychology*. Routledge and Kegan Paul, London.

Sherman, P. S. (1989) A micro-based decision support system for managing aggressive case management programs for treatment resistant clients. *Computers in Human Services*, **4** (3–4), 181–90.

Sherman, P. S. and Porter, R. (1991) Mental health consumers as case management aides. *Hospital and Community Psychiatry*, **42** (5), 494–8.

Showalter, E. (1987) *The Female Malady*. Virago Press, London.

Slade, P. D. (1990) The behavioural and cognitive treatment of psychotic symptoms, in Bentall, R. P. *Reconstructing Schizophrenia*. Routledge, London.

Smith, H. (1990a) *Developing Individual Services in the Community*. Discussion paper. University of Kent, Canterbury.

Smith, H. (1990b) *Lessons from America: Some Aspects of the Holyoke/ Chicopee Service*. Unpublished manuscript. University of Kent, Canterbury.

Smith, H. and Mansell, J. (1991) *The Quest for Quality: Searching for the Holy Grail*. Discussion paper. University of Kent, Canterbury.

Smith, J. and Birchwood, M. (1990) Relatives and patients as partners in the management of schizophrenia. *British Journal of Psychiatry*, **156**, 654–60.

Social Services Inspectorate (1991) *Care Management and Assessment: Manager's Guide*, HMSO, London.

Speilberger, C. D., Gorsuch, R. L. and Lushene, R. E. (1970) *Manual for the State Trait Anxiety Inventory*. Consulting Psychologist Press, Palo Alto.

Stein, L. I. and Test, M. A. (1980) Alternative to mental hospital treatment I. *Archives of General Psychiatry*, **37**, 392–7.

Stevenson, O. and Parsloe, P. (1978) *Social Service Teams. The Practitioner's View*. HMSO, London.

Stroul, B. (1989) Community support programmes for people with long-term mental illness: a conceptual framework. *Psychosocial Rehabilitation Journal*, **12** (3), 9–26.

Tarrier, N. (1990) The family management of schizophrenia, in Bentall, R. P. *Reconstructing Schizophrenia*. Routledge, London.

Tarrier, N. (1991) Behavioural psychotherapy and schizophrenia. *Behavioural Psychotherapy*, **19** (1), 121–30.

Taube, C. A., Morlock, L., Burns, B. J. and Santos, A. B. (1990) New directions in research on assertive community treatment. *Hospital and Community Psychiatry*, **41** (6), 642–7.

Test, M. A. and Stein, L. I. (1980) Alternative to mental hospital treatment III. Social cost. *Archives of General Psychiatry*, **37**, 409–12.

Thornicroft, G. (1991) The concept of case management for long-term mental illness. *International Review of Psychiatry*, **3**, 125–32.

Timms, P. W. and Fry, A. H. (1989) Homelessness and mental illness. *Health Trends*, **21**, 70–1.

Townsend, P. and Davidson, N. (1982) *Inequalities in Health*. Penguin, London.

Turner, T. (1988) Community care. *British Journal of Psychiatry*, **152**, 1–3.

Vass, P. (1990) Principles and practice of devolved budgets, in Allen, I. (ed.)*Care Managers and Care Management*. Policy Studies Institute, London.

Waldron, G. (1981) Picking up the pieces. *Health and Social Service Journal*, 12 June, 708–10.

Warner, R. (1985) *Recovery from Schizophrenia*. Routledge and Kegan Paul, Boston.

Watts, F. and Bennett, D. (1983) Management of the staff team, in Watts, F. and Bennett, D. (eds.) *Theory and Practice of Psychiatric Rehabilitation*. Wiley, Chichester.

Watzlawick, P., Weakland, J. and Fisch, R. (1974) *Change: Principles of Problem formation and Problem Resolution*. Norton, New York.

Weisbrod, B. A., Test, M. A. and Stein L. I. (1980) Alternative to mental hospital treatment II. Economic benefit-cost analysis. *Archives of General Psychiatry*, **37**, 400–5.

Weller, M. P. I. (1989) Mental illness – who cares? *Nature*, **339**, 249–52.

Welsh Office Social Services Inspectorate (1990) *Community Care: Draft Guidance on Assessment and Case Management*. Welsh Office.

West, M. A. and Farr, J. L. (1989) Innovation at work: psychological perspectives. *Social Behaviour*, **4**, 15–30.

West, M. A. and Farr, J. L. (1990) *Innovation and Creativity at Work*. Wiley, Chichester.

White, E. and Brooker, C. (1990) The future of community psychiatric nursing: what might the care programme approach mean for practice and education? *Community Psychiatric Nursing Journal*, **10** (6), 27–30.

Williams, J. and Watson, G. (1988) Sexual inequality, family life and family therapy, in Street, E. and Dryden, W. *Family Therapy in Britain*. Open University Press. Milton Keynes.

Wistow, G. (1990) *Community Care Planning: A Review of Past Experiences and future Imperatives*. Nuffield Institute for Health Services Studies, Leeds.

Witheridge, T. F. and Dincin, J. (1985) The Bridge: an assertive outreach team in an urban setting. *New Directions for Mental Health Services*, **26**, 65–76.

Witheridge, T. F., Dincin, J. and Appleby, L. (1982) Working with the most frequent recidivists: a total team approach to assertive resource management. *Psychosocial Rehabilitation Journal*, **5**, 9–11.

Wolowitz, D. (1983) Clients' rights in a case management system, in Sanborn, C. J. *Case Management in Mental Health Services*, Haworth Press, New York.

World Health Organization (1988) *International Classification of Diseases, Draft for 10th Revision*. WHO, Geneva.

Zubin, J. and Spring, B. (1977) Vulnerability – a new view of schizophrenia. *Journal of Abnormal Psychology*, **86**, 103–26.

Subject index

Author index